Applied
Anatomy & Physiology
Second Edition
A Case Study Approach

**Workbook &
Laboratory Manual**

BRIAN R. SHMAEFSKY, PhD

KINGWOOD COLLEGE
KINGWOOD, TEXAS

EMC
Publishing

St. Paul

Contributing Writer: Scott Schaeffer
Content Expert: Melissa Curfman-Falvey
Senior Editor: Carley Fruzzetti
Production Editor: Sarah Kearin
Cover and Text Designer: Leslie Anderson
Senior Design and Production Specialist: Jaana Bykonich
Illustrators: Graphic World; S4Carlisle Publication Services

Care has been taken to verify the accuracy of information presented in this book. However, the authors, editors, and publisher cannot accept responsibility for Web, e-mail, newsgroup, or chat room subject matter or content, or for consequences from application of the information in this book, and make no warranty, expressed or implied, with respect to its content.

Trademarks: Some of the product names and company names included in this book have been used for identification purposes only and may be trademarks or registered trade names of their respective manufacturers and sellers. The authors, editors, and publisher disclaim any affiliation, association, or connection with, or sponsorship or endorsement by, such owners.

Photo Credits: Chapter 1: *n/a;* **Chapter 2**: *n/a;* **Chapter 3**: *Page 38 top* CMSP, *bottom* Centers for Disease Control/Dr. W. Winn; **Chapter 4**: *n/a;* **Chapter 5**: *Pages 62 through 72* A.D.A.M., a business unit of Ebix 2012; **Chapter 6**: *Pages 88 through 96* A.D.A.M., a business unit of Ebix 2012; **Chapter 7**: *Pages 112 through 119* A.D.A.M., a business unit of Ebix 2012; *Page 123* CMSP, *Page 124 top* CMSP, *bottom* CMSP; **Chapter 8**: *n/a;* **Chapter 9**: *Pages 150 through 162* A.D.A.M., a business unit of Ebix 2012, *Page 168 top* RUET STEPH/CORBIS SYGMA, *bottom* CMSP; **Chapter 10**: *Pages 178 through 184* A.D.A.M., a business unit of Ebix 2012; **Chapter 11**: *Pages 199 through 212* A.D.A.M., a business unit of Ebix 2012; **Chapter 12**: *Pages 227 through 231* A.D.A.M., a business unit of Ebix 2012; **Chapter 13**: *Pages 246 through 254* A.D.A.M., a business unit of Ebix 2012; **Chapter 14**: *Pages 272 through 275* A.D.A.M., a business unit of Ebix 2012; **Chapter 15**: *Pages 293 through 297* A.D.A.M., a business unit of Ebix 2012

Additional Practice content courtesy of A.D.A.M, a business unit of Ebix 2012.

Laboratory Safety & Best Practices pages adapted from *Biotechnology: Laboratory Manual* by Ellen Daugherty

We have made every effort to trace the ownership of all copyrighted material and to secure permission from copyright holders. In the event of any question arising as to the use of any material, we will be pleased to make the necessary corrections in future printings. Thanks are due to the aforementioned authors, publishers, and agents for permission to use the materials indicated.

ISBN 978-0-82196-362-3

© 2013 by EMC Publishing, LLC
875 Montreal Way
St. Paul, MN 55102
Email: educate@emcp.com
Website: www.emcschool.com

Printed in the United States of America

21 20 19 18 17 16 15 14 13 12   1 2 3 4 5 6 7 8 9 10

TABLE OF CONTENTS

PREFACE

The *Applied Anatomy & Physiology Workbook & Laboratory Manual* is designed to accompany the *Applied Anatomy & Physiology, A Case Study Approach* textbook. The chapters of this *Workbook & Laboratory Manual* are designed to reinforce and assess your knowledge of anatomy and physiology through a series of activities and lab exercises specially designed to evaluate those skills. Completion of the activities will enhance your learning experience and allow you to identify your strengths and weaknesses regarding the material you have learned in the textbook.

Workbook & Laboratory Manual Contents

Each chapter of the *Workbook & Laboratory Manual* contains the following features:

- **Completion exercises:** Complete a series of sentences by filling in each blank with a key term from the text.
- **Matching:** Match a list of terms with the corresponding descriptions.
- **Complete the Terms Tables:** Fill in the missing key terms and/or definitions in the table.
- **Label the Graphic exercises:** Locate and label specific parts or features in an illustration of an element of the human body and answer related questions to reinforce your understanding.
- **Color the Graphic exercises:** Color the different parts of an anatomical illustration according to the color key provided.
- **Practical Application questions:** Complete a series of short answer questions designed to assess your ability to apply what you have learned to practical, clinical-based scenarios.
- **Laboratory Activities:** Reinforce and extend your knowledge of chapter concepts by performing laboratory-based, hands-on activities with the assistance of your classroom instructor.
- **Quizzes:** Complete a 25-question multiple choice quiz designed to assess your understanding of the material you learned in the chapter.

Additional Practice from A.D.A.M. Interactive Anatomy

Chapters 5 through 7 and 9 through 15 of the *Workbook & Laboratory Manual* include a section called "Additional Practice." These pages contain related content from A.D.A.M. Interactive Anatomy. Although it is not necessary to use A.D.A.M. Interactive Anatomy to complete this section, access to the website will enhance your learning experience. Additional A.D.A.M. Interactive Anatomy activities and resources referenced within this workbook may include:

- Atlas Anatomy
- 3D Anatomy
- Clinical Animations
- Clinical Illustrations
- Multimedia Encyclopedia

A link to access A.D.A.M. Interactive Anatomy online can be found on the Internet Resource Center (www.emcschool.net/anatphys). This link will take you to a page where you can obtain a pin code and will also direct you to the A.D.A.M. Interactive Anatomy website. Once you have obtained a pin code, you may want to bookmark the A.D.A.M. Interactive Anatomy website for faster access.

Resources

When completing the exercises in this text, it may be helpful to reference the accompanying student textbook, *Applied Anatomy & Physiology, A Case Study Approach*. Each workbook chapter complements the textbook subject matter, and the corresponding exercises reinforce the concepts presented in class. With the permission of your instructor, accessing the A.D.A.M. Interactive Anatomy website will also help to strengthen and increase your knowledge of the information presented in the textbook, especially when completing the Additional Practice sections.

LABORATORY SAFETY & BEST PRACTICES

As an anatomy and physiology student, you may conduct laboratory and field investigations. Critical thinking and problem-solving skills applied to scientific methods will assist you in your work both in and out of the classroom. Scientists who work in a laboratory are expected to follow standard laboratory operating procedures. These operating procedures include skills that are critical for safety such as following written and oral instructions, working in a professional manner, keeping detailed records of all work, and using all equipment and instruments accurately and as directed. As students you may need to collect and organize qualitative and quantitative data and take accurate and precise measurements using tools such as calculators, spreadsheets, microscopes, and other equipment. The laboratory activities that are included in this manual will help you to learn some of the most basic standard laboratory operating procedures. These include:

- Understanding safety concerns, precautions, equipment, and rules for a typical laboratory facility
- Setting up experiments, documenting conditions, analyzing data, and reporting results

Laboratory instruments and equipment are delicate and expensive. Chemicals and biological solutions can be dangerous if you do not handle them correctly and follow specific safety protocols. It is also critical to learn to follow laboratory procedures exactly, to document your observations, and to document the conditions and results of each experiment, test, or reaction.

How to Document Laboratory Activities

Scientific experiments must be well documented. Although your instructor may allow you to record your laboratory activity results on a regular sheet of paper or in a file on your computer, laboratory employees are required to document experiments and other activities in a legal scientific notebook. In the United States, the first person to conceive and show diligence to develop an invention, product, or process is awarded the patent for that product or process. Notebooks that are properly prepared, maintained, and witnessed are legal evidence of conception and diligence to practice an invention. A protocol has been posted on the Internet Resource Center (IRC) to help you set up and maintain a legal scientific notebook. Go to www.emcschool.net/anatphys to access this document. Here are some general tips to use when creating your own laboratory notebook:

Setting Up a Laboratory Notebook

1. Obtain a bound notebook with sewn pages. A composition-style notebook works well.
2. Graphs and other small sheets of paper may be pasted into your notebook when necessary.
3. Make page 1 the title page. In the middle of the page, in bold print, write:

[Name of course] NOTEBOOK

Course section or class period

Name of school

Your name

Today's date

Also write this information on the front cover of your notebook.

4. Unless noted otherwise, write all entries in black permanent ink. The use of colored pens or pencils is acceptable in some cases, as approved by your instructor.
5. Do not erase, ink over, or white out any errors. Draw a single line through errors so they can still be read.
6. Write clearly so there is no ambiguity about the information recorded. Skip lines between data tables, graphs, and important conclusions to make it easier to find and read recorded information.

Additional Data Recording Methods for Anatomy & Physiology

The subjects of anatomy and physiology will require you to create and analyze charts, diagrams, graphs, and other graphic organizers. The laboratory activities provided in this text include charts and figures for you to analyze and will require you to record your data using spreadsheets, charts, and graphs. A collection of graphic organizers is available on the Internet Resource Center for your use as well. You can use these graphic organizers for your laboratory activities as well as with investigations done both in and out of the classroom to make predictions, compare data, identify sequences of events, and more.

Laboratory Safety: Protecting Yourself and Others

A laboratory may have several safety hazards. These can put you in danger as well as place the safety of others at risk. It is your responsibility to know and follow the basic laboratory safety rules; to recognize and understand the hazardous materials, equipment, and conditions in a facility; and to work to reduce potential risks.

In the event of an accident, you must know what to do to minimize the damage that might occur. This includes knowing the location of emergency equipment and how to use it.

Basic Laboratory Safety Rules

1. No eating or drinking in the laboratory. No gum chewing. No makeup application.
2. Wear safety apparel such as safety goggles, gloves, lab coats, and other protective clothing as necessary. Tie hair back if using Bunsen burners.
3. Know the location of eyewash stations, fire exits, fire extinguishers, and safety showers.
4. Wash hands regularly, especially after working with microorganisms, human body fluid samples, or chemicals.

5. Be aware of potential dangers. Before using products or equipment, carefully read labels, experimental protocols, and equipment instructions and literature. Know the location of and how to read Material Safety Data Sheets (MSDS) if they are provided. Material Safety Data Sheets are created by product and solution manufacturers to instruct consumers on proper handling and safety.

6. Contaminated samples (chemical, biological, glass, etc.) must be disposed of in appropriate containers. Do not pick up broken glass with your hands. Learn the specific methods from your lab instructor.

7. Label all samples and reagents clearly with the name of the item, the name of the person who prepared the sample, and the date of preparation.

8. Know emergency phone numbers and the best way to contact the facility safety officer.

9. Report spills and accidents to your instructor immediately.

10. Know how to properly dispose of or recycle materials used in the laboratory.

11. If you are taking antibiotics, or you are pregnant or ill, report your condition to your supervisor.

12. Practice conservation of materials and use all materials and equipment carefully.

13. Handle all sharp objects with care.

Although the lab activities presented in this text do not include dissection, an anatomy and physiology student will likely be expected perform dissection during his or her studies. Safety procedures specific to dissection include the following:

- Gloves must be worn at all times; safety goggles are also highly recommended.
- The specimen should be thoroughly rinsed before beginning dissection.
- Avoid exposing eyes, mouth, or other parts of the body to chemicals used in preserving the specimen.
- Firmly secure the specimen to the dissection tray using pins or other appropriate materials.
- Handle the scalpel with care and cut away from yourself and others.
- Properly dispose of (or store) the specimen and organs as instructed.
- Clean and disinfect your lab area and tools.
- Wash your hands thoroughly with soap and water.

In summary, a person who demonstrates good laboratory practices will:

- Know the location and use of all the personal protective equipment, such as goggles, gloves, hoods, etc.
- Know the location and proper use of all the emergency equipment, such as Material Safety Data Sheets (MSDS), chemical showers, safety eyewash, fire extinguishers, etc.
- Maintain a clean (and sterile, when appropriate) workspace that is free from clutter.
- Recognize chemical and biological hazards. Know how to handle and dispose of each hazard properly.
- Know who to contact and how to contact emergency services in the case of a fire, chemical, or biological emergency.

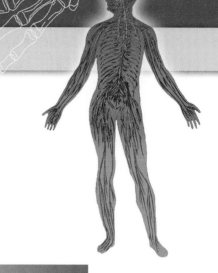

CHAPTER

OVERVIEW OF THE BODY

Introduction

Chapter 1 of the student textbook introduced you to the common language used by those in the health care field, as well as the importance of using precise language when describing parts, regions, and positions of the body. The following exercises and lab activities will help you apply the terms used in the study of the human body. If you need assistance with completing the activities in this chapter, refer to Chapter 1 of *Applied Anatomy & Physiology, A Case Study Approach*. The labeled figures and key terms will assist you in answering the questions in each activity. In addition, access to A.D.A.M. Interactive Anatomy will provide you with the opportunity to expand on your understanding of the concepts presented in the textbook.

Completion

Complete the following sentences by filling in each blank with a key term from the text.

1. Anatomical study can be divided into areas of _____ anatomy and _____ anatomy.

2. The anatomical and physiological study of human disease is called _____.

3. The terms that describe the way a body can be divided into parts by imaginary cuts are known as _____ _____.

4. The terms medial, superior, and distal are examples of terms of _____ _____.

5. A movement term that describes the opposing movement of another part is said to be _____.

6. Body region terms can be divided into three categories known as _____ _____, _____ _____, and _____.

7. The terms *superficial* and *deep* belong to the category of _____ _____.

8. The term *umbilical* is the name of one of the _____ _____.

9. The two major anterior body cavities are the _____ and _____, and the two major posterior body cavities are the _____ and _____.

10. The thoracic cavity can be further divided into the _____ and _____ cavities.

Matching

Match each of the following descriptions with the corresponding term by writing the letter of the description on the blank next to the term.

a) lying on the back

b) movement away from the body

c) often used in place of the term *anatomy*

d) farther from the point of attachment

e) beneath or lower than

f) creates left and right sections

g) refers to the outer layer or surface covering

h) located on both sides of the body

i) surrounding the heart

j) body region above the stomach

k) body region containing the stomach

_____ abduction

_____ bilateral

_____ distal

_____ epigastric

_____ inferior

_____ morphology

_____ parietal

_____ pericardial

_____ sagittal plane

_____ supine

_____ abdominal

Complete the Terms Table

Fill in the missing key terms and/or definitions in the following table.

Term	Definition
	anatomical and physiological study of human growth
cephalic	
	farther from the midline
	creation of superior and inferior sections
extension	
visceral	
	clinical body position with patient supine and legs bent
	body cavity containing the heart and lungs
	spinal column region of the neck
peritoneum	

Label the Graphic

Identify each of the following directional orientation terms in the illustration below. Write the number of the term in the box nearest to the arrow indicating its location. Finally, answer the anatomical position questions that follow.

1. anterior
2. distal
3. inferior
4. lateral
5. medial
6. posterior
7. proximal
8. superior

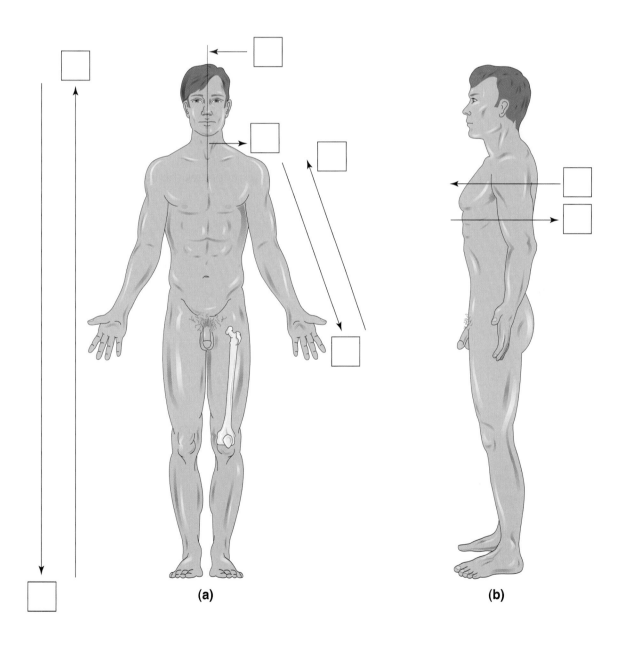

(a)   (b)

1. Which term best describes the location of the eyebrows with respect to the eyes?

2. Where are the toes in comparison to the knees?

3. The elbow is _____ to the wrist.

4. In relation to the sternum (breastbone), which term describes the location of the arms?

5. In anatomical position, which term locates the little finger in relation to the thumb?

6. What term describes the view of the body in Figure A?

7. Where is the chin is relation to the mouth?

8. If Figure A were turned in the opposite direction, which view of the body would be seen?

Color the Graphic

Color this illustration using the following color key:

cranial – blue
spinal – yellow
thoracic – red
abdominal – green
pelvic – purple

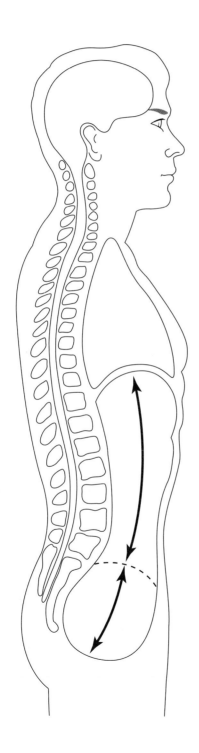

Write brief responses to the following scenarios.

1. List the parts of the hand that would be described by different directional orientation terms if the subject were standing with the palms flat against the legs rather than in standard anatomical position.

2. Identify five body parts or organs that are bilaterally located.

3. Name a clinical body position that might be used for each of the following medical situations:

   a) spinal adjustment

   b) gynecological exam

   c) dental examination of the upper jaw

   d) blood-pressure measurement

   e) abdominal surgery

4. Apply directional plane terms to each of the following descriptions:

   a) slicing a carrot in coin-like sections

   b) cutting a pineapple perfectly in half so that each portion contains the stem

   c) cutting a pickle into many thin lengthwise (longitudinal) slices

d) sawing a bed in two so that the headboard is separated from the foot-board

5. Identify the body movement term involved in each of the following activities:

a) "squat" exercises

b) jumping jacks

c) "pigeon-toe" placement of the feet

6. In which abdominopelvic quadrant might a patient with cirrhosis (inflammation of the liver) experience observable swelling?

Which abdominopelvic region(s)?

7. Would it be correct to use abdominopelvic region terms to describe pain associated with the heart? Why or why not?

8. Which of the body cavities are connected? Explain.

9. In which major body cavity do you think the conditions called pleuritis and pericarditis would occur?

10. Name the spinal-column region with which each of the following items would have the most contact when worn:

   a) belt

   b) choker necklace

   c) strapless bikini top

   d) hip pockets

Laboratory Activity 1

Drawing the Abdominopelvic Regions & Quadrants

Background

It is important to be able to visualize the abdominopelvic regions of the body without having to reference a book. This activity will give you practice identifying the precise locations of these regions on an illustration of the human body.

Materials

- Blank overhead transparency sheet
- Washable black marker
- Washable red marker

Procedure

Place the clear transparency sheet over the diagram provided here. First, use the black marker to draw the lines representing the abdominopelvic regions. Then, label the diagram. Next, use the red marker to draw the quadrant lines. Add the quadrant labels. Compare your drawing and labels to the information provided in this chapter.

Figure 1.1 Abdominopelvic Regions and Quadrants

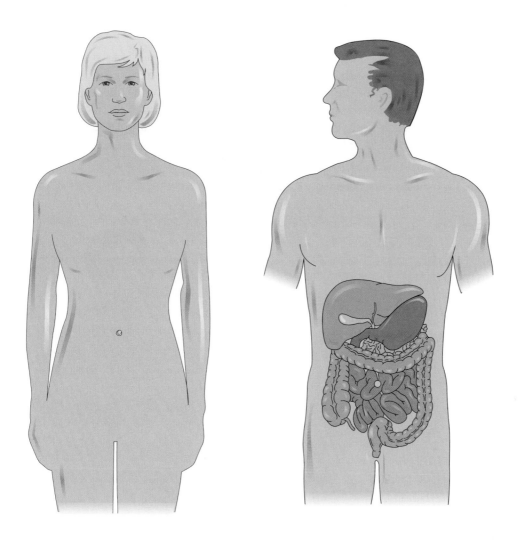

Laboratory Activity 2

Drawing the Body Cavities

Materials

- Blank overhead transparency sheet
- Washable black marker
- Blank sheet of paper

Procedure

Place the transparency sheet over the diagram provided here. Use the marker to draw the outlines of the body cavities on the transparency sheet. Then label the cavities. Next, on the blank piece of paper, make a list of the major structures found in each body cavity. Compare your drawings and labels with the information provided in this chapter.

Figure 1.2 Location of Body Cavities

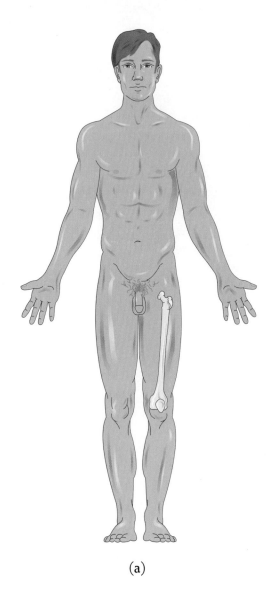
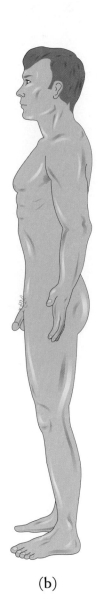

(a)   (b)

Quiz

1. List the opposite directional orientation term for each of the following:

    a) inferior

    b) medial

    c) distal

    d) posterior

2. What is the name for each of the following clinical body positions?

    a) lying face down

    b) lying on the back

    c) sitting with the legs straight out, with the back supported

    d) lying on the back with the legs bent

    e) bending on the knees with the face down

3. Write the antagonist for each of the following body movements:

    a) extension

    b) abduction

    c) inversion

4. Name the four quadrants used in body-region terminology.

5. Name the nine abdominopelvic regions.

6. What is the difference between anatomy and physiology?

7. Define the term *directional plane*.

8. Observing a human tissue sample under a microscope would be an example of what division of anatomical study?

9. Describe proper anatomical position.

10. Anterior and posterior body sections are created by which kind of directional plane?

11. Distinguish between the terms *proximal* and *distal*.

12. What is the name given to the anatomical and physiological study of diseases?

13. Which type of plane creates equal-sized left and right halves?

14. Give an example of a flexion movement.

15. Use the correct term of directional orientation to describe the position of the arms in relation to the trunk of the body (in anatomical position).

16. Give an example of a superficial body structure.

17. List the two major anterior body cavities and their respective subdivisions.

18. List the posterior body cavities.

19. What does the parietal peritoneum touch?

20. Define the term *visceral*.

CHAPTER

2

THE BODY'S CHEMICAL MAKEUP

Introduction

Approximately 96% of the human body is composed of just four elements: carbon, hydrogen, oxygen, and nitrogen. Organic chemistry is the study of those chemicals that contain carbon in their structure, while biochemistry is the study of how those organic molecules work together within an organism. Chapter 2 of the student textbook explores the chemical makeup of the body and how the nutrients we eat supply the needed energy to allow our bodies to function harmoniously. The following exercises and lab activities will require you to apply what you have learned regarding the chemical structure of the human body. If you require assistance when completing the activities, refer to Chapter 2 of *Applied Anatomy & Physiology, A Case Study Approach*. The labeled figures and key terms will assist you in answering the questions in each activity. Access A.D.A.M. Interactive Anatomy for additional information and opportunities to deepen your understanding of the concepts presented in the textbook.

Completion

Complete the following sentences by filling in each blank with a key term from the text.

1. The branch of natural science that deals with the composition of substances that make up a living organism's body structures, as well as their properties and reactions in body function, is called _____ _____ or _____ _____.

2. The structure of each element consists of two major components called the atomic _____ and the atomic _____.

3. Two or more atoms joined together by chemical bonds form a _____.

4. Attached to the carbon skeleton of a biochemical is a _____ _____, which is responsible for its chemical activity.

5. Molecules that have the same _____ formula but differ in their _____ formulas are called isomers.

6. The four organic chemical groups into which human molecules are categorized are _____, _____, _____, and _____ _____.

7. Lipids are commonly categorized into three groups: _____, _____, and _____.

8. Carbohydrates are classified as _____, _____, or _____ based on the number of "units" of which they are composed.

9. Small chains of amino acids form _____, and larger chains form _____.

10. A nucleotide has three parts: the _____ _____, _____ _____, and a _____ _____ _____.

Matching

Match each of the following terms with the corresponding description by placing the letter of the term on the blank next to the correct description.

a) atomic number

b) atomic mass

c) element

d) glycemic index

e) hydrophilic

f) nucleotide

g) organic

h) terpenoids

i) tertiary

j) triglyceride

_____ primary fat stored in the human body

_____ building block of nucleic acids

_____ 3-D structure of a protein

_____ sum of the number of protons and neutrons

_____ cannot be chemically broken down

_____ containing carbon

_____ water soluble

_____ category of fat in which vitamins belong

_____ measure of available glucose in food

_____ number of protons in the nucleus

Complete the Terms Table

Fill in the missing key terms and/or definitions in the following table.

Term	Definition
	elements that have the same number of protons but differ in neutron number
ion	
	anything that has mass and occupies space
	an alcohol functional group
buffer	

continued

Term	Definition
monomer	
	having a stronger negative or positive charge on one side
	a fatty acid lacking hydrogen atoms and possessing double bonds
hydrogenate	
	a form of glucose stored in the liver and muscles
free-radical	
	the aging process of an organism

Label the Graphic

Complete each of the following activities, using the illustrations below. Then asnwer the questions that follow.

1. Identify the type of chemical bond represented in each of the two illustrations by writing the correct term, either *ionic* or *covalent*, beneath each picture.
2. Using the Periodic Table in Figure 2.2 (page 32 of the text), identify each atom shown by writing the symbol used to represent its elemental name in the space directly above it. (Hint: Notice that the number of protons is indicated by the letter *P* inside each atom.)
3. In the ionic bond, indicate the ionic charge present on each of the atoms after bonding. (Hint: Which subatomic part has changed in number for each atom, and how does it affect the electrical charge present on the atom?) Write the ionic charge directly beneath each atom.

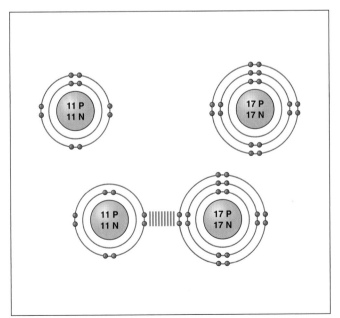

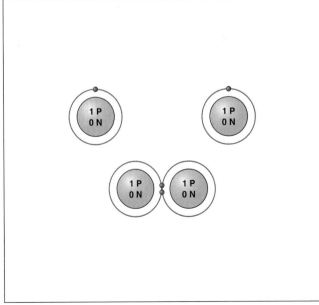

1. What is the atomic mass of the Na atom illustrated on the previous page?

2. How many electrons exist in the outer orbital of each atom after ionic bonding?

3. Which subatomic particle is absent in the H atoms illustrated? Does this have any affect on their electrical charge?

4. Are the H atoms ions? Explain.

Color the Graphic

Color this illustration using the following color key:

electrons –purple
protons – red
neutrons – green
atomic nucleus – circle in blue
atomic orbitals – highlight in yellow

Write brief responses to the following scenarios.

1a. Hydrogen is the first element on the periodic table, and it has an atomic number of 1.008. What does this tell you about each subatomic part?

1b. What additional information can you determine about a subatomic particle by knowing its atomic mass?

2. The atomic weight of an element is the average of all possible isotopes (considering the naturally occurring proportion of each isotope). The atomic weight of hydrogen is 1.008. Which isotope of hydrogen (^{1}H, ^{2}H, or ^{3}H) do you think is most abundant in nature? Explain.

3. If a chemical reaction is defined as the interaction between two or more substances to form a new product, does adding salt (NaCl) to water result in a chemical reaction? Why or why not?

4. If grapefruit juice has a pH of 3.0 and egg whites have a pH of 8.0, which contains more H^+ ions? How many more?

5. Imagine that you are a research and development scientist working for a food manufacturing company. To create a new product, you need to use a fat that contains short carbon chains and is low in saturation. You have three frozen containers of lard, butter, and unhydrogenated vegetable oil, but the labels have fallen off, and you do not know which container holds which fat. Explain a simple way to choose the one to use. (You cannot rely on color, smell, or taste.)

6. A friend of yours decides to start taking a multivitamin. She assumes that more is better, so she increases her dosage to three tablets per day, rather than the manufacturer-recommended dose of one per day. What advice would you give her?

7. Can all carbohydrates containing glucose supply that molecule as an energy source for the body? Explain.

8. Many digestive enzymes are made in the pancreas and sent to the small intestine, where they break down food molecules. The stomach has a very low pH compared with the intestine, and precedes the intestine in the digestive tract. If the pancreas were unable to produce digestive enzymes, would it be possible to ingest pancreatic enzymes and still maintain the same level of digestion? Explain.

9. Since most people know that humans need oxygen to survive, they might conclude that oxygen is always "good" for the body. Respond to this idea, given what you have learned about the factors involved in senescence.

✿A.D.A.M. Education

Refer to the Encyclopedia section of A.D.A.M. Interactive Anatomy to open the A.D.A.M. Multimedia Encyclopedia. A quick search of key terms from the textbook will help you reinforce the knowledge you have gained thus far. Try entering terms such as *carbohydrates, fat, protein,* or *malnutrition* in the search bar to read more about these vital parts of the body's chemical makeup.

10. Do you think it would be beneficial to add antioxidants to sunscreen to increase its effectiveness in preventing sun damage?

Laboratory Activity 1

Sources of Glucose

Background

As you learned in this chapter, simple sugars, such as glucose, are a primary source of quick energy for the body. However, large amounts of simple sugars taken in at one time can elevate blood sugar. This, in turn, can create immediate problems for the body (such as damage to the blood vessels and kidneys). The body must find a way to remove the sugars from the blood before they damage the blood vessels and kidneys. This excess glucose is stored away as glycogen. Excessive consumption of glucose in the diet can lead to the conversion of glucose to fat. People with diseases such as diabetes have trouble removing glucose from the blood. Therefore, they have to be very careful about the glucose content of the foods they eat.

This activity provides a simple way to look for glucose in various foods and beverages. It uses the chemical reaction in which the carbonyl functional group of glucose interacts with an indicator solution in a urine test strip.

Materials

- Three glucose test strips for urine sugar testing
- Sharp scissors
- Marker
- Two eyedroppers

- Small container of water
- Six small plastic cups
- Three metal teaspoons
- One slice of potato
- One grape
- One small bottle of colorless soda
- One small piece of ground beef
- One small bottle of orange juice

Setup

Use the marker to label the six cups as follows: 1) control; 2) potato; 3) grape; 4) soda; 5) meat; and 6) juice. Then, cut each of the urine test strips in half lengthwise so that you have six narrow strips with a colored test patch on the bottom. Use the marker to label each of the six strips as follows: 1) "C" for control; 2) "P" for potato; 3) "G" for grape; 4) "S" for soda; 5) "M" for meat; and 6) "J" for juice. Now, set up the experiment as follows:

1. Add a dropper full of water to the "C" cup.
2. Use a clean spoon to grind up the piece of potato in the "P" cup.
3. Use a clean spoon to grind up the grape in the "G" cup.
4. Use a clean eyedropper to add a dropper full of soda to the "S" cup.
5. Use a clean spoon to grind up the meat in the "M" cup.
6. Use a clean eyedropper to add a dropper full of juice to the "J" cup.

Challenge

Before conducting the laboratory activity, write a brief paragraph describing what you think the results will be. Use the information you learned in Chapter 2 of the student textbook to support your view.

Procedure

Place the appropriately labeled test strips next to each cup. Then, dip the colored portion of the test strip into the liquid in the cup. Compare any changes to the urine test strip with the color chart on the test-strip container. Record how much glucose is present in each substance.

Analysis

Write an analytical paragraph that describes your original expectations about the glucose content of each food and whether the results supported your expectations. In your essay, identify how one might use the information you obtained to help people make dietary choices. Identify possible examples.

Laboratory Activity 2

Factors That Affect the Glycemic Index of Food

Background

Recall from this chapter that the glycemic index is a measure of how fast a particular food elevates the blood sugar level after eating. Foods with a high glycemic index are loaded with simple sugars, such as glucose. Starch has a somewhat lower glycemic index than glucose, but it is still a major source of "hidden" simple sugars in the diet. In this activity, you will use the iodine test to indicate the presence of starch in certain foods. Iodine indicates the presence of starch by turning from an amber or brown color to a dark blue or black color.

Materials

- Bottle of medicinal iodine solution (potassium iodide)
- Marker
- Eyedropper
- Small container of water
- Seven 3-inch by 3-inch squares of aluminum foil
- One slice of uncooked potato
- One slice of baked potato
- One slice fresh yellow banana
- One slice of artichoke heart
- One slice of cauliflower
- One slice of Jerusalem artichoke or taro

Setup

Use the marker to label the seven squares of aluminum foil as follows: 1) control; 2) uncooked potato; 3) cooked potato; 4) banana; 5) artichoke; 6) cauliflower; and 7) Jerusalem artichoke or taro.

1. Add a dropper full of water to the "control" square.
2. Add the slice of uncooked potato to the "uncooked potato" square.
3. Add the slice of cooked potato to the "cooked potato" square.
4. Add the slice of banana to the "banana" square.
5. Add the slice of artichoke to the "artichoke" square.
6. Add the slice of cauliflower to the "cauliflower" square.
7. Add the slice of Jerusalem artichoke or taro to the appropriately labeled square.

Procedure

Add one drop of the iodine solution to the samples on each square. Make sure the iodine solution is mixed with the water and soaked into each sample of food. Look for the presence of starch by watching for the change in color of the iodine solution. The control should not change color. As mentioned above, foods with starch will turn the iodine solution blue or black.

Analysis

Write a brief analysis of the laboratory experiment in which you answer the following questions:

1. Which of the foods contain starch?
2. How should these findings influence dietary choices about the intake of foods with a low glycemic index?
3. Some people assume that baking starchy foods lowers the glycemic index. Was this confirmed or refuted by your findings?

1. Organic chemistry is the study of chemicals that:
   a) only occur naturally
   b) are only found in living organisms
   c) contain the element carbon
   d) All of the above

2. An atom is:
   a) the smallest portion of an element that still retains its properties
   b) composed of subatomic particles
   c) consists of a nucleus surrounded by orbitals
   d) All of the above

3. The hydroxyl group:
   a) is chemically shown as OH
   b) helps molecules dissolve in water
   c) is also known as an alcohol group
   d) All of the above

4. Molecules that have the same chemical formula, but that differ in structural formula are:
   a) always similar in their physical and chemical properties
   b) called isomers
   c) cannot be classified as biochemicals
   d) All of the above

5. A common functional group containing nitrogen is called the:
   a) carboxyl group
   b) carbonyl group
   c) sulfate group
   d) amino group

6. Acids are:
   a) electron acceptors
   b) lower than 7.0 on the pH scale
   c) chemically shown as OH
   d) All of the above

7. Which of the following terms are the most similar in meaning?
   a) fat soluble/hydrophilic
   b) fat insoluble/hydrophobic
   c) fat soluble/lipophobic
   d) fat insoluble/lipophobic

8. Cholesterol is a:
   a) protein
   b) nucleic acid
   c) carbohydrate
   d) lipid

9. Which of the following terms are the most similar in meaning?
   a) monomer nucleotide/RNA
   b) polymer nucleotide/ATP
   c) polymer nucleotide/DNA
   d) All of the above

10. Single units of carbohydrates are joined by _____
    bonds to form polysaccharides, while amino acids are linked by
    _____ bonds to form polypeptides.
    a) ionic/protein
    b) chiral/nucleotide
    c) glycosidic/peptide
    d) All of the above

11. Which one of the three categories of lipids is most abundant in the body?
    a) terpenoids
    b) sterols
    c) glycerides
    d) All are contained in similar amounts

12. Which of the following is *not* a monosaccharide?
    a) glucose
    b) maltose
    c) fructose
    d) galactose

13. Nucleotide monomers are involved in:
    a) determining genetic traits
    b) transferring energy
    c) making proteins
    d) All of the above

14. What product of carbohydrates and fats is most important for the body?
    a) energy
    b) amino acids
    c) structural material
    d) electrolytes

15. A diet lacking proper nutrition might cause:
    a) malnutrition
    b) undernutrition
    c) cravings
    d) All of the above

16. Which of the following best describes senescence?
    a) the process of body aging brought about by molecular decay
    b) the result, in part, of free radical oxidation
    c) the result, in part, of the effects of ultraviolet radiation
    d) All of the above

17. List the subatomic parts that contribute to each of the following:

    a) atomic number   _____   _____

    b) atomic mass   _____   _____

    c) atomic bonding   _____   _____

    d) isotopes   _____   _____

    e) ions   _____   _____

18. Match each protein level of organization with the letter of the term or phrase to which it is most related.

    a) 3-D arrangement   _____ primary structure

    b) linear amino-acid arrangement   _____ secondary structure

    c) helix or sheet   _____ tertiary structure

    d) two or more polypeptide chains   _____ quaternary structure

19. List two sources of free radicals.

20. List four functions of fat in the body.

21. List four common disaccharides. Which common monosaccharide is present in all four?

22. Briefly explain what is meant by the polarity of an H_2O molecule.

23. Why are buffers important in the human body?

24. What is the difference between an element and a compound? Give an example of each. Would it be correct to say that they are both formed from molecules?

25. Why are covalent bonds the most common bonds in biochemicals?

3 Organization of the Body

Introduction

The human body is a complex organism that depends on the interrelationship of its eleven organ systems to maintain homeostasis. Chapter 3 of the textbook explores the structure and function of the cell before introducing you to the four tissue types found within the human body: epithelial, connective, muscle, and nerve tissue. These four tissues form the organs that contribute to the eleven body systems constantly working in unison to maintain the overall homeostasis of the body. The following exercises and lab activities will allow you to practice what you have learned regarding the organization of the human body and the interrelationship of its systems. Refer to Chapter 3 of *Applied Anatomy & Physiology, A Case Study Approach* if you need assistance. The labeled figures and key terms will assist you in answering the questions in each activity. Access A.D.A.M. Interactive Anatomy for additional information that will provide an opportunity to deepen your understanding of the concepts presented in the textbook.

Completion

Complete the following sentences by filling in each blank with a key term from the text.

1. The physiological environment of a cell includes both the _____ and _____ environments.

2. If a molecule has gained an electron through a chemical reaction, it has been _____ , and if it has lost an electron, it has been _____ .

3. Chemical reactions that use up energy are called _____ , while those that release energy are _____ .

4. Movement of molecules across the cell membrane following the diffusion gradient is _____ transport, while movement going against the diffusion gradient is _____ transport.

5. A cell will gain water when it is in a(n) _____ environment, and it will lose water when it is in a(n) _____ environment.

6. The three divisions of cell structural components are the _____ _____ , the _____ , and the _____ .

7. Metabolic reactions that use energy to build body components are called _____ , while those that break down molecules to provide energy and raw materials needed for such activity are called _____ .

8. _____ takes place in the cytoplasm, but the remaining stages of aerobic respiration occur in the _____ .

9. Gene expression consists of two stages: _____ and _____ . _____ occurs in the nucleus, during which DNA is copied to create messenger ribonucleic acid (mRNA). _____ occurs in the cytoplasm on organelles called _____ and synthe-sizes _____ .

10. Sexual cell division is called meiosis. It occurs in two nuclear divisions: The first separates _____ chromosomes, and the second sepa-rates _____ .

11. The four major types of human tissue are _____ , _____ , _____ , and _____ .

12. _____ glands, which release their secretions into the blood, and _____ glands, whose secretions travel through ducts to particular body locations, are both composed of _____ cells.

13. Connective tissue can be classified as _____ , such as blood, or _____ , such as bone, _____ , _____ , and ten-dons.

14. The three types of muscle tissue are _____ , _____ , and _____ .

15. _____ is a decrease in the size of a cell, tissue, or organ, while the enlargement of these body components is known as _____ .

16. The telomeres, or chromosome ends, of cancer cells do not undergo short-ening following _____ (cell division), thus enabling them to be immortal.

Matching

Match each of the following terms with the corresponding description by placing the letter of the term on the blank next to the correct description.

a) anaphase

b) blood

c) calorie

d) chromatid

e) codon

f) epithelium

g) fatty change

h) gamete

i) lymphatic

j) metabolism

k) necrosis

l) neuroglia

m) oxidative phosphorylation

n) product

o) prokaryotic

p) skeletal

q) secretion

r) stratified

s) telomere

_____ stage of karyokinesis during which chromosomes separate

_____ the outcome of a chemical reaction

_____ the end of a chromosome

_____ standard unit of heat

_____ type of exocytosis

_____ lacks organelles and possesses a nucleoid genome

_____ sum of all chemical reactions in the body

_____ process driven by the electron transport chain to produce ATP

_____ three nucleotides coding for a specific amino acid

_____ egg or sperm

_____ multilayered

_____ tissue that forms a lining or covering in the body

_____ type of connective tissue

_____ voluntary muscle tissue

_____ nervous tissue cell

_____ body system that fights disease

_____ localized tissue death

_____ can occur from excessive alcohol intake

_____ a copy of a chromosome

Complete the Terms Table

Fill in the missing key terms and/or definitions in the following table.

Term	Definition
cell	
	substance that dissolves other chemicals
organ	
substrate	
	passive transport process that utilizes carrier proteins to move molecules across a semipermeable membrane
	the potential of water to move across a selectively permeable membrane
heredity	
	a strand of DNA that actually codes for genes
somatic cells	
haploid	
amyloid	
	an embryological germ layer that forms bone and muscle
	cells that do not undergo differentiation into embryological germ layers, but retain their ability to differentiate
pseudostratified	
	a condition in which diseased cells move from one location to another, continuing their abnormal function at the new site

Label the Graphic

Identify each of the following in the illustration of DNA function below. Write the name of the term in the box indicating its location.

1. transcription
2. translation
3. gene
4. pre-mRNA
5. mRNA (at two locations)
6. protein
7. ribosome
8. RNA

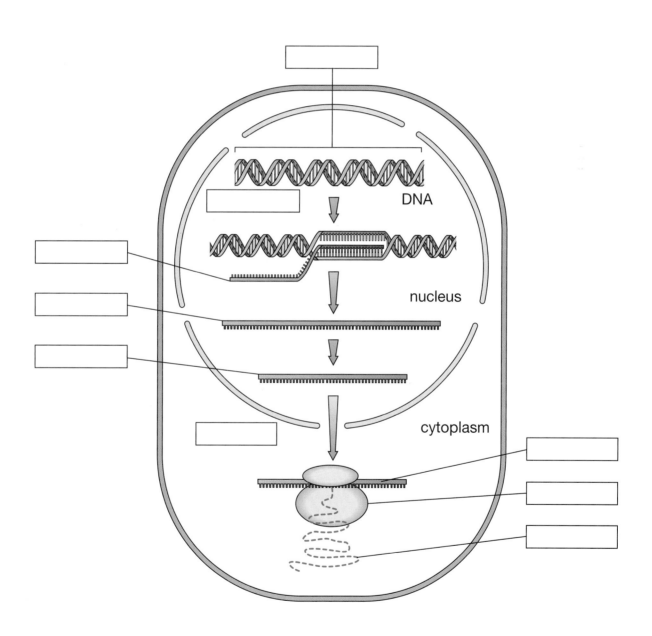

Color the Graphic

Color this illustration using the following color key:

cytoplasm — yellow
DNA — black
Golgi apparatus — dark green
lysosome — grey
mitochondrion — orange
nuclear membrane — brown
nucleolus — dark blue
nucleus — light blue
ribosomes — red
RNA — white
rough endoplasmic reticulum — light green
smooth endoplasmic reticulum — pink

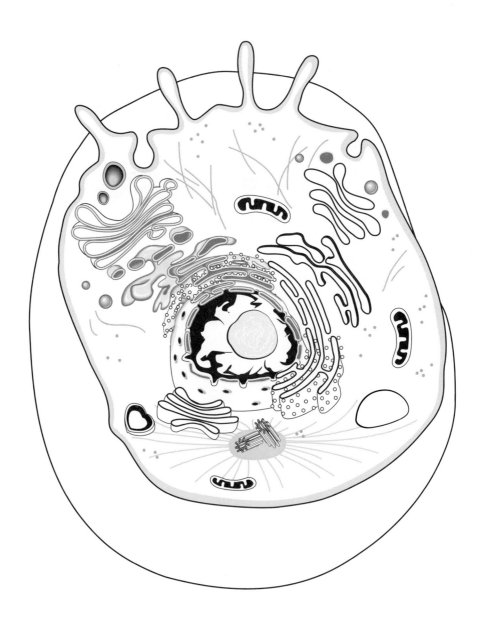

Practical Application

Write brief responses to the following scenarios.

1. Do unicelluar organisms such as bacteria and yeast cells exhibit differentiation? Explain.

2. Why is water such an ideal substance for the body's physiological environment?

3. In terms of energy conversion, how is the energy needed by a weight lifter created, and what type of energy does his or her activity create?

4. What do you think would happen to an individual's red blood cells if the osmolarity of the plasma (liquid portion of the blood) was altered by continuous intravenous administration of pure water containing no electrolytes?

5. The text states that "Today it is accepted that not all living organisms have a cell as the basic unit of structure." Give an example of one such organism that is considered to be living, and apply what you have learned about cell structure to substantiate why it does not have true cells.

6. Do you think that an individual's body would undergo more anabolic metabolism or more catabolic metabolism following a meal high in carbohydrates? Briefly explain.

7. A common form of Down's syndrome (a disease predestined at conception that results in physical anomalies and mental retardation) is caused by a genetic defect called *trisomy* in which a particular chromosome in the affected individual's genome is present in triplicate, rather than in the diploid (paired) state of normal chromosomes. This means that either the egg or the sperm creating the offspring carried a diploid number of this chromosome in a gamete, rather than the normal haploid number. Use your knowledge of cell division to determine which type of cell division would cause the genetic defect to occur. In which stage of division would this defect most likely happen?

8. A lab technician prepared slides of tissue samples and forgot to label their source in the body. One is from a patient's heart wall and the other is from the stomach wall. What visual clues might help differentiate the two samples?

9. What is the difference between dysplasia and hyperplasia?

10. When asked about the role that telomeres play in cellular aging, a student replies that this part of the chromosome makes proteins that initiate cellular death. Is this statement true? Explain why or why not.

Laboratory Activity 1

Identifying Cell Structure and Function

Background

Early histologists looked at microscopic preparations of body structures to determine the function of a particular tissue. They observed the composition of cell types in the specimen and used this information to draw conclusions about the specimen's role in the body. It takes a trained eye to recognize the different cell types in a tissue or organ specimen. The following activities will help you practice looking for cells in tissue and organ samples.

Materials

- Blank overhead transparency sheet or tracing paper
- Microscope with high power capability (400X)
- Prepared slide of skin
- Prepared slide of trachea

Microscope Safety Precautions and Tips

- Always carry a microscope with both hands (hold the arm with one hand and support the base with the other).
- When adjusting the objective lens do NOT allow the lens to touch the slide. Doing so may cause the slide to break.
- When using a monocular microscope, avoid eye strain by looking through the eyepiece with one eye and keeping the other eye open.
- Do not touch glass lenses with your fingers. Only lens paper should be used.
- Contents of a slide will appear upside down and backwards.

Procedure and Analysis

Place the slide of the skin on the stage, centered over the light path, and fasten the slide with slide clips, if available. Adjust the objective lens by first looking at the slide and lens from the side of the microscope. Lower the objective lens (using the coarse adjustment) close to the stage without touching the slide. Look through the eyepiece and adjust the light source for the greatest visibility. Slowly turn the coarse adjustment so that the objective lens goes up (away from the slide) and continue until the image comes into focus. Use the fine adjustment, if available, for further focusing. You may need to adjust the slide so that the image is centered.

Can you find the layers of squamous cells that compose the outer portion of the skin? How do the cells in the outermost layer of skin differ from those below it? Is it possible to see a transition in tissue structure as you view inner regions of the skin? What happens to the cellular composition of the innermost layers of skin? What does this tell you about the function of the innermost layers compared with that of the outer layers?

Next, look at the prepared slide of trachea under the microscope. Adjust the lens and slide as necessary. Can you identify cells in this specimen that were not present in the skin sample? What is the probable function of this structure based on the cell types present?

Now, look at the photographs on the next page and answer the questions below each figure.

Figure 3.1

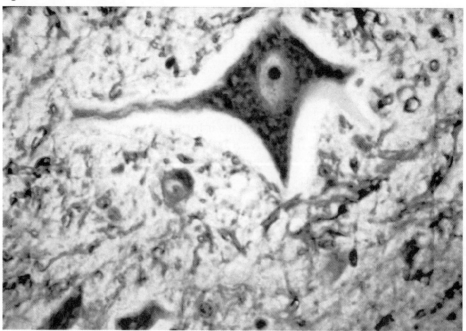

Figure 3.1 Analysis

In a paragraph, answer the following questions: What types of cells can be seen in this figure? What is the appearance of the matrix surrounding the cells? What body structure is most likely the origin of this specimen?

Figure 3.2

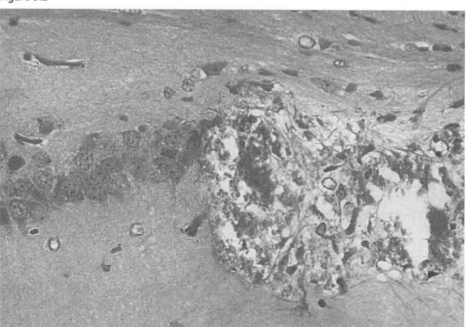

Figure 3.2 Analysis

In a paragraph, answer the following questions: How does Figure 3.2 compare with Figure 3.1? What are the similarities and differences? What could be the probable cause of the differences noted in the two specimens?

Laboratory Activity 2

Effects of Aspirin on Cell Function

Background

Aspirin and caffeine are bioactive molecules that affect cell function. Many plants produce aspirin or acetylsalicylic acid to control cellular metabolism. Caffeine is another substance produced by plants to regulate their metabolism. Many of these plant chemicals are produced to alter the metabolism of animals that eat the plants as well. This laboratory activity looks at the effects of aspirin and caffeine on a model cell. The cell model being investigated in this activity is the cytoskeleton of an aquatic plant called elodea. Plant cells can be used in certain human investigations because they have many similar metabolic processes as human cells. Usually, cytoskeleton physiology varies very little between different types of cells.

Materials

- Elodea or American waterweed, kept in a container of clean fresh water
- Forceps for removing elodea leaf
- Three aspirin tablets, ground up and soaked in 1 tablespoon of water
- One teabag, soaked in 1/2 cup of cool water
- Microscope
- Two droppers for collecting samples aspirin and tea solutions
- Two clean microscope slides
- Surgical gloves

Precautions

Wear surgical gloves when handling the aspirin and caffeine solutions. All of the solutions can be stored in labeled bottles in the refrigerator for two or three weeks. Excess should be flushed down a drain.

Procedure

Remove two leaves of elodea and place them on separate clean microscope slides. Observe the cells of one specimen under the microscope at high magnification and look for the movement of small green spots. These spots are plant organelles called chloroplasts. They are attached to the cell's cytoskeleton. Plant cells use the cytoskeleton as a conveyor belt to move chloroplasts and other cell components around the cytoplasm. Make sure you keep adding water to the slides to keep them from drying out and dying. Keep track of the speed and direction at which the chloroplasts are moving around the cell.

Add one drop of the aspirin solution to the leaf on the slide. While observing the leaf, record anything that happens to the movement of the chloroplasts. It may take one or two minutes for the aspirin to enter the cells. Add another drop or two of aspirin and see if this has any other effect. Next, look at the second elodea specimen. This time, add one drop of caffeine to the slide after observing the chloroplast movement. Again, record what happens to the movement of the chloroplasts. Add another drop or two of caffeine to see if it has any different effect.

Analysis

Use your observations from the laboratory activity to analyze the effects of aspirin and caffeine by answering the following questions:

1. How do aspirin and caffeine affect the cytoplasmic function you observed?
2. What is the effect of adding an additional drop of aspirin or caffeine to the slide?
3. How do the effects of aspirin differ from those of caffeine?
4. How could this data be interpreted to better understand the effects of aspirin or caffeine on human cells?
5. What information is available on the Internet about the effects of aspirin and caffeine on cell function?

 Quiz

1. The level of human organizational hierarchy one step above the cellular level is the:
   a) molecular level
   b) organ level
   c) tissue level
   d) envirome level

2. Conditions that influence homeostasis of the aqueous environment of cells are determined by:
   a) pH
   b) chemical reactions
   c) molecular transport across the membrane
   d) All of the above

3. Food is a form of _____ energy, which provides the ability for muscle movement, which is a form of _____ energy.
   a) electrical/mechanical
   b) thermal/kinetic
   c) chemical/potential
   d) potential/kinetic

4. In the chemical reactions of aerobic respiration, what molecule is the initial substrate?
   a) acetyl coA
   b) glucose
   c) pyruvic acid
   d) starch

5. Which waste product, produced in large amounts by a diet high in protein and low in carbohydrate content, can lead to dehydration in the body?
   a) glycerol
   b) carboxyl
   c) urea
   d) amino acids

6. The region of an enzyme that is the point of its attachment to another molecule is called the:
   a) amine bond
   b) protein activator
   c) ionization point
   d) active site

7. If the content of nitrogen in a cell's environment is isotonic to the cell's interior, this means that:
   a) there is no movement of nitrogen into or out of body cells
   b) nitrogen will travel across the cell membrane in both directions at a similar rate
   c) there is more nitrogen in the air than in the cell's interior
   d) there is less nitrogen in air than in the cell's interior

8. Facilitated diffusion requires the use of:
   a) active transport
   b) osmosis
   c) carrier proteins
   d) All of the above

9. Excretion and secretion are examples of:
   a) diffusion
   b) active transport pumping
   c) passive transport
   d) bulk active transport

10. The human body is:
   a) composed of eukaryotic cells
   b) described as unicellular
   c) composed of prokaryotic cells
   d) All of the above

11. Proteins in the cell membrane:
   a) help provide cell communication
   b) can be involved in molecular transport
   c) aid in cell adhesion
   d) All of the above

12. Which of the following best describes the order of aerobic respiration?
   a) glycolysis → Krebs cycle → fermentation
   b) electron transport chain → Krebs cycle → glycolysis
   c) fermentation → glycolysis → Krebs cycle
   d) glycolysis → Krebs cycle → electron transport chain

13. In gene expression, transcribed DNA would be best described as:
   a) a gene
   b) polypeptide
   c) mRNA
   d) translated DNA

14. Which of the following terms is *not* one of the four major human tissue types?
    a) glandular
    b) epithelial
    c) connective
    d) nervous

15. Epithelial tissues are categorized by:
    a) shape and size
    b) layering and shape
    c) number of nuclei
    d) All of the above

16. On the line next to each of the processes below, write the letters of the terms that pertain to it.

    mitosis: _____

    meiosis: _____

    a) gamete formation
    b) somatic cells
    c) haploid products
    d) diploid products
    e) asexual reproduction
    f) sexual reproduction

17. Match each event of the cell cycle with the phase in which it occurs:
    a) DNA replication   _____ anaphase

    b) equatorial plane   _____ cytokinesis

    c) differentiation   _____ G_0

    d) chromatid or chromosome   _____ interphase
       separation
                                            _____ metaphase
    e) spindle fiber formation
                                            _____ prophase
    f) cytoplasmic division

18. Match each of the following terms with the letter of the most appropriate description:
    a) increase in cell size   _____ amyloid deposition

    b) abnormal growth pattern   _____ atrophy

    c) decrease in cell size   _____ dysplasia

    d) Alzheimer's disease   _____ hyperplasia

    e) increase in cell number   _____ hypertrophy

19. In respect to the hierarchy of human structure, arrange the following terms in order from lowest to highest: atom, body systems, cell, molecule, organism, organ, society, and tissue.

20. What roles do ions play in the body's physiological environment, and how can they be lost from the body?

21. List the parts of a cell that are interrelated by their function of producing and transporting molecules and/or cell parts.

22. The body's physiological environment can be described as a mixture, or _____, composed of water, which is the _____ portion, and the _____ component, which comprises the dissolved bio-chemicals.

23. The three types of muscle tissue are known as _____, _____, and _____.

24. Connective tissue types are classified as either _____ or _____.

25. Because they lack the ability to undergo mitosis, fat-, skeletal-, and ner-vous-tissue cells are subject to damage in the cytoplasm, which is called _____ _____ _____.

THE SKIN AND ITS PARTS

Introduction

The integument, or skin, is the largest organ in the human body. The skin, hair, nails, and specialized sweat and oil glands combine to form the integumentary system. The integumentary system protects the internal structures of the human body, helps regulate body temperature, offers protection against the harmful ultraviolet rays of the sun, and even produces secretions to keep bacteria at bay and maintain optimum skin moisture. The following exercises and lab activities will require you to apply what you have learned regarding the skin and its parts. Refer to Chapter 4 of *Applied Anatomy & Physiology, A Case Study Approach* for assistance, if necessary. Access A.D.A.M. Interactive Anatomy for additional information and opportunities to deepen your understanding of the concepts presented in the textbook.

Completion

Complete the following sentences by filling in each blank with a key term from the text.

1. The outermost layer of skin forms from the embryological germ layer _____, and develops into _____ _____ epithelial tissue.

2. The three layers of human skin, from deep to superficial, are _____, _____, and _____.

3. The bulk of the dermis is composed of loose connective tissue known as _____, which contains the fibers _____, _____, and _____.

4. The innermost layer of the epidermis is known as the _____ _____.

5. The four categories of skin appendages are _____, _____, _____, and _____.

6. The _____, _____, and _____ glands are commonly found in the skin.

7. The skin's ability to detect environmental stimuli is due to its many specialized nerve cells, which are called _____ _____.

8. Fingernails and toenails are composed of the protein _____.

9. The integumentary system provides the body protection from three types of environmental damage: _____, _____, and _____.

10. Two categories of skin aging factors are known as _____ and _____.

Matching

Match each of the following terms with the corresponding description by placing the letter of the term on the blank next to the correct description.

a) commensals

b) furuncle

c) hair medulla

d) hair papilla

e) inherent

f) lipoma

g) lunula

h) sebum

i) stratum corneum

j) stratum lucidum

k) tinea

l) vitiligo

_____ inborn

_____ associated with thick skin

_____ skin and hair "oil"

_____ outermost epidermal layer

_____ white "half-moon" portion of the fingernail

_____ hair follicle base

_____ inner layer of hair

_____ beneficial skin bacteria

_____ fat-cell tumor

_____ inflammation of hair follicles

_____ condition of hypopigmention

_____ ringworm

Complete the Terms Table

Fill in the missing key terms and/or definitions in the following table.

Term	Definition
angiogenic factor	
malpighian layer	
	a layer of epidermis that contains immune system cells
	inflammation of the fibrous connective tissue of the subcutaneous layer of skin
pheromones	
	pain-sensing structures that are distributed throughout the lower part of the epidermis
	touch receptors found in the mucus membranes of the mouth
arrector pili muscle	
	nerve cells that convert environmental stimuli into body signals
	a burn category that characterizes reparable damage of the stratum spinosum and stratum generativum layers of the epidermis
solar lentigenes	
	a group of viruses that cause warts in humans

Label the Graphic

Identify each of the following terms in the illustration below. Write the number of the skin appendage in the box indicating its location.

1. subcutaneous (adipose) tissue
2. hair shaft
3. dermis
4. eccrine sweat gland
5. epidermis
6. hair follicle
7. sebaceous gland
8. stratum corneum
9. stratum germinativum

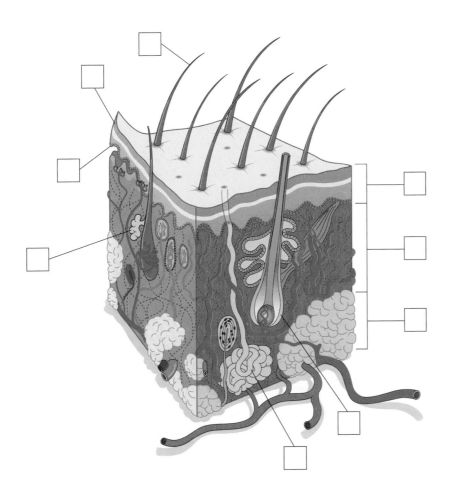

A.D.A.M. Education

Refer to the Clinical Illustrations section of A.D.A.M. Interactive Anatomy for additional information on common conditions associated with the integumentary system. Click the Clinical Illustrations tab and narrow your search by choosing *Integumentary* from the Body System menu. A quick search will lead you to a variety of images to explore including the layers of the skin, types of burns, skin grafts, decubitus ulcers (bedsores), the hair follicle, baldness, and skin cancers.

Color the Graphic

Color this illustration using the following color key:

adipose tissue (subcutaneous layer) – yellow
arrector pili muscle – purple
dermis – brown
epidermis – pink
hair bulb – red
hair follicle – orange
hair papilla – blue
hair shaft – black
sebaceous gland – green

Practical Application

Write brief responses to the following scenarios.

1. A child asks you why his lips "turn blue" when it is cold outside. What would you say to this child to answer his question?

2. How might a lower-than-normal fibroblast cell population affect an individual's skin?

3. A person sitting next to you in a steam room inquires as to why it feels hotter in the steam room than it does in the dry sauna, even though both areas are kept at the same temperature. How would you respond to this question?

4. A student has recently learned that pheromones are secreted by sweat glands, and he wants to design a study to investigate whether or not certain animals are affected by human pheromones. He plans to collect sweat from the headbands and gloves worn by individuals undergoing strenuous exercise to use in his study. Will this be an effective method for his study? Why or why not?

5. A friend says that his family only uses soaps and shampoos that contain added antibacterial agents. Explain to him why this might not be such a good idea.

6. A friend of yours is trying to lose weight and has started a diet that excessively restricts calories. She has also begun an extremely vigorous exercise program. At the same time, she has noticed that her hair seems to be thinning, so she has been brushing it often in hopes of stimulating its growth. What factors might be contributing to your friend's hair loss?

7. Investigators often collect hair for forensic analysis. What information can be obtained through hair analysis?

8. An entrepreneur is excited about his idea to develop a body lotion that totally prevents body sweating. Explain to him why it would not be advisable to pursue the development of this product.

9. If third-degree burns result in irreparable damage to the deeper layers of skin where pain receptors are found, why do victims of severe burns still experience pain?

10. A friend of yours wears cosmetics on her face every day. She always removes her makeup by washing her face, and she then applies a variety of astringents and moisturizers. She often boasts that her meticulous skin care habits are much healthier than your more "natural" approach to beauty. Do you agree?

A.D.A.M. Education

Refer to the Encyclopedia section of A.D.A.M. Interactive Anatomy to open the A.D.A.M. Multimedia Encyclopedia. A quick search of key terms from the textbook will help you reinforce the knowledge you have gained thus far. Look up pathological terms such as *impetigo, tinea, psoriasis,* and *acne* in the search bar to read more about these important topics regarding the skin and its parts.

Laboratory Activity 1

Histology of the Integumentary System

Background Information

As a fetus develops, the skin forms particular structures in specific areas of the body. This differentiation is what gives the hair on the head a different appearance than the hair on the rest of the body, for example. The skin also adapts to conditions imposed on a particular region. For example, the skin on the sole of the foot is subject to different conditions than the skin on the back of the arm, but both of these skin areas become slightly modified in response to environmental exposure and the pressure placed on them during day-to-day living. Scientists and physicians are able to look at the skin structure under a microscope to see if it is functioning normally in a particular region. However, to do this they must have a database of microscopic skin images for comparison. Activities such as the one provided below are used to train physicians and technicians to use image databases to identify skin disorders.

Materials

- Microscope with high-power capability (400X)
- Prepared slide of human skin – normal or thin section
- Prepared slide of human skin – with hairs
- Prepared slide of human skin – thick skin or callus
- Computer with access to the Internet

Procedure and Analysis

Open your computer's web browser and go to the University of Michigan's Medical Histology and Virtual Microscopy website at http://anatphys.emcp. net/UMVirtualMicroscopy. This will open the Virtual Slide List for Medical Histology Course. Navigate to the section titled EPITHELIAL TISSUE, which provides information about the human integument. Click on the various plates to view microscopic images of skin from different body regions.

Normal Skin Place the slide containing the normal skin under the microscope. Start with the low magnification, and move to the higher magnification to see individual cells. Can you find the three layers of skin by comparing the slide with the plantar skin images (slides 106 and 107) provided on the website? Draw a simple picture showing the relative thickness of each skin layer, making sure to include the epithelial cells. Are any other skin structures or appendages visible in the atlas images that are not evident in the slide?

Skin with Hair Look at the specimen of the skin with hair under the microscope. How does it compare with the slide of the normal skin? Besides the hair, are there any structures in this skin section that were not present in the normal skin? Use the Virtual Microscopy website to find the part of the body where this skin section is most likely found.

Thick Skin/Callus Place the thick skin specimen on the microscope and view the various regions of the skin. How do these areas compare with those on the normal skin and the skin with hair? What environmental factors or body conditions cause this skin to differ from the normal skin? What causes the skin to become so thick? Use the Virtual Microscopy website to compare and contrast the epithelium of the skin to the epithelium found in other body structures such as the esophagus, kidney, and small intestine.

Laboratory Activity 2

Effectiveness of Sunscreen at Blocking Ultraviolet Light

Background

Recall that the skin secretes melanin into the epidermis in an attempt to block the damaging rays of ultraviolet light from reaching the lower layers of skin. This is most effective in people with dark or tanned skin, but even in those people, melanin does not stop all the ultraviolet light from penetrating the inner layers of skin. Sunscreen provides an additional layer of protection against ultraviolet light, but not all sunscreens are equally effective. This activity provides a way to test the effectiveness of sunscreens and other chemicals at blocking ultraviolet light.

Materials

- Ultraviolet (black) light
- Black permanent marker
- Bright yellow highlighter marker
- Black sheet of paper (8 1/2 in x 11 in)
- Five clean microscope slides
- Ten small corks
- Small bottle of sunscreen rated SPF 10
- Small bottle of sunscreen rated SPF 60
- Small bottle of hand lotion
- Small bottle of shampoo
- Digital camera (optional)
- Surgical gloves (optional)

Precautions

You should wear surgical gloves when handling the chemicals in this activity, in case of allergies or sensitivities to a particular product. Never aim the ultraviolet light at the eyes or the skin. The black light should not be stared into for more than a few seconds. Slides should be cleaned with warm, soapy water and then reused.

Procedure

Use the yellow highlighter marker to draw an 11-inch line through the middle of the black paper. Turn on the ultraviolet light, and hold it over the center of the black piece of paper. The line should glow brightly in response to the ultraviolet light. This glow is called *fluorescence* and is due to the interaction of the ultraviolet light with light-absorbing chemicals in the highlighter ink. The ultraviolet light excites electrons in the light-absorbing chemicals, and the excited electrons emit light when they return to their normal condition in the chemical. Now, use the black marker to label the slides with the numbers 1–5. Prop the five slides on the corks so that they each sit over the yellow line, as shown in Figure 4.1. Make sure the slides are arranged in numbered order. There should be little or no space between the slides.

Gently smear slide 2 with the SPF 10 sunscreen. Apply the SPF 60 sunscreen to slide 3, the hand lotion to slide 4, and the shampoo to slide 5. Next, shine the ultraviolet light over the slides and note whether the highlighter glows. The brighter the glow, the more ultraviolet light is passing through the substance.

Figure 4.1

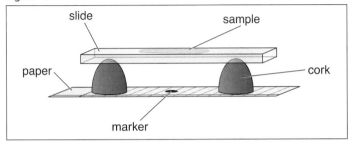

Analysis

Answer the following questions in a brief analytical essay that describes the results of the lab:

1. Does glass block ultraviolet light? To what degree?

2. How does this activity demonstrate the effectiveness and benefits of sunscreen in blocking ultraviolet light?

3. To what degree do hand creams and shampoos block ultraviolet light?

4. How might this activity be used to teach others about the importance of using and understanding sunscreens?

Quiz

1. The four functions of skin, in order of importance, are:
   a) protection, waste excretion, sensation, and heat regulation
   b) sensation, heat regulation, protection, and sweating
   c) protection, respiration, heat regulation, and sensation
   d) protection, heat regulation, sensation, and waste excretion

2. Which of the following is an adaptive feature of skin?
   a) hair growth
   b) nail formation on the fingers and toes
   c) callus formation
   d) All of the above

3. From which of the embryological germ layers does the dermis develop?
   a) ectoderm
   b) mesoderm
   c) endoderm
   d) All of the above

4. Which of the following can contribute to hair loss?
   a) genes
   b) stress
   c) excessive exercise
   d) All of the above

5. Which of the following correctly names the layers of skin in order from superficial to deep?
   a) epidermis, dermis, hypodermis
   b) dermis, hypodermis, epidermis
   c) epidermis, endodermis, dermis
   d) hypodermis, dermis, epidermis

6. The dermal layer of skin contains:
   a) loose areolar connective tissue
   b) elastin, collagen, and reticular fibers
   c) skin appendages
   d) All of the above

7. Which of the following is *not* associated with the hypodermis or subcutaneous layer?
   a) keratin
   b) adipose
   c) fascia
   d) nerves

8. The area of the fingers and toes where nail growth takes place is called the:
   a) nail matrix
   b) lunula
   c) nail plate
   d) nail root

9. Which of the following describes hair?
   a) modified stratum corneum
   b) a shaft composed of an inner medulla and an outer cortex
   c) "colored" by keratin and/or melanin
   d) All of the above

10. Which of the following word pairs describing human hair is correct?
    a) pubic : body hair
    b) vellus : fetal/infant hair
    c) terminal : head hair
    d) lanugo : genital hair

11. Mechanical damage to the skin is minimized by which of the following?
    a) callus formation
    b) microorganisms
    c) sebum production
    d) All of the above

12. Commensal organisms:
    a) are undesirable for healthy skin
    b) help keep disease-causing organisms from thriving on the skin
    c) are not commonly found on healthy skin
    d) All of the above

13. The skin regulates body heat through which of the following?
    a) the control of blood flow in vessels
    b) evaporation of sweat
    c) adipose tissue insulation
    d) All of the above

14. What are the primary structures of waste excretion in the skin?
    a) eccrine sweat glands
    b) apocrine sweat glands
    c) sebaceous glands
    d) All of the above contribute equally

15. Third-degree burns:
    a) involve only the superficial layers of the skin
    b) are defined as damage to the stratum germinativum
    c) usually heal through skin regeneration
    d) commonly involve nerve cell loss in the dermis

16. Skin cancer:
    a) is a degenerative skin disorder
    b) has an underlying genetic component
    c) is induced by sunlight or chemical exposure
    d) All of the above

17. The most common bacterial skin infections are caused by which of the following?
    a) dermatophytes
    b) *Candida albicans*
    c) *Staphylococcus aureus*
    d) All of the above

18. Skin aging:
    a) causes homeostasis disruption that contributes to overall body aging
    b) is due to both intrinsic and extrinsic factors
    c) is characterized by many gross anatomical changes
    d) All of the above

19. Match each of the following descriptions of the layers of the epidermis with the name of the layer it describes:

    a) generates upper layers   _____ dermal papilla layer

    b) connects epidermis to dermis   _____ malpighian layer

    c) contains immune cells   _____ stratum basale

    d) melanin deposition   _____ stratum compactum

    e) associated with thick skin   _____ stratum corneum

    f) desquamation   _____ stratum granulosum

    g) keratocyte origination   _____ stratum lucidum

    h) single layer of keratinized cells _____ stratum spinosum

20. Match each of the following skin sensory receptors with the corresponding description:

a) free nerve endings _____ touch receptors in the fingertips

b) Krause's end bulbs _____ receptors of pressure or constant touch

c) Meissner's corpuscles _____ pain sensory receptors

d) Merkel cells _____ deep tactile receptors of the hypodermis

e) pacinian corpuscles _____ tactile receptors in the dermal papilla

f) Ruffini's receptors _____ tactile receptors of the mouth

21. Match each of the following types of benign skin tumors with the corresponding description:

a) lipoma _____ rough, greasy, dark growth

b) moles _____ adipose tissue

c) sebaceous hyperplasia _____ pigmented squamous cells

d) seborrheic keratosis _____ sweat gland ducts

e) syringomas _____ oil glands

22. Name two accessory structures of hair, and describe the function of each.

23. List the three types of glands commonly found in the skin, as well as their respective secretions and body locations.

24. List the components of the integumentary system.

25. What benefits do cerumen and sebum have for the body?

THE SKELETAL SYSTEM

Introduction

The skeletal system is composed of bones, cartilage, and ligaments that give shape to the body, protect internal structures, and provide support and sites of attachment for other tissues. A joint is formed when two bones come together and tendons connect muscles to the bones, allowing for movement. Bones require a certain amount of stress to remain healthy. A sedentary lifestyle or poor diet can contribute to bone weakening and make bones more susceptible to fracture. The following exercises and lab activities will require you to apply what you have learned about the skeletal system. For assistance, refer to Chapter 5 of *Applied Anatomy & Physiology, A Case Study Approach*. Access A.D.A.M. Interactive Anatomy for additional information to deepen your understanding of the concepts presented in the textbook.

Completion

Complete the following sentences by filling in each blank with a key term from the text.

1. The human skeleton is divided into two major groups: the _____ division and the _____ division.

2. The skull is composed of two groups of bones: _____ and _____.

3. The sutures of the skull are the _____, _____, _____, and _____.

4. The five regions of the vertebral column are _____, _____, _____, _____, and _____.

5. The thoracic skeleton includes the _____ _____, _____, and _____.

6. Bones can be categorized into four types of shapes: _____, _____, _____, and _____.

7. A joint can be _____ classified into one of three types known as _____, _____, or _____; or it can be _____ classified as a _____, _____, or _____ joint.

8. All human bones (except teeth) can be classified as either _____ or _____.

9. The two types of bone marrow are _____, which contains fat cells, and _____, which contains _____ cells.

10. The two major types of embryological bone formation are _____ ossification and _____ ossification.

Matching

Match each of the following terms with the corresponding description by writing the letter of the term on the blank next to the correct description.

a) articulation   _____ immovable joint

b) bursa   _____ bone cells

c) capitate   _____ ends of long bones

d) communited   _____ bone tissue building cells

e) epiphyses   _____ synovial fluid-filled sac

f) hyoid   _____ bone surface connective tissue

g) ossification   _____ arch-shaped bone under lower jaw

h) osteoblasts   _____ formed within a tendon

i) osteocytes   _____ the process of bone formation

j) palatine   _____ bone junction

k) patella   _____ fracture causing bone displacement

l) periostium   _____ articulates with tibia and fibula

m) sesamoid bone   _____ carpal bone

n) synarthrosis   _____ kneecap

o) talus   _____ roof of the mouth

Complete the Terms Table

Fill in the missing key terms and/or definitions in the following table.

Term	Definition
wormian bones	
	the main body of a long bone
	a passageway for nerves and blood vessels from the periostium to the haversian canal
canaliculi	
	soft fat-cell tissue found within most bones
	cells that break down bone and cartilage during bone development and repair
rheumatoid arthritis	
fibromyalgia	
	the socket of the pelvic girdle forming the articulation point with the femur
pubic symphysis	
	soft areas on the infant skull that are the result of incomplete development of the intramembranous bone
angulation	

Label the Graphic

Identify each of the following in the illustration below. Write the number of the bone in the box indicating its location.

1. carpals	8. metacarpals	14. pubis
2. clavicle	9. patella	15. scapula
3. cranium	10. radius	16. sternum
4. femur	11. pectoral (shoulder)	17. tibia
5. fibula	girdle	18. ulna
6. humerus	12. pelvic girdle	19. vertebral column
7. ischium	13. phalanges	20. xiphoid process

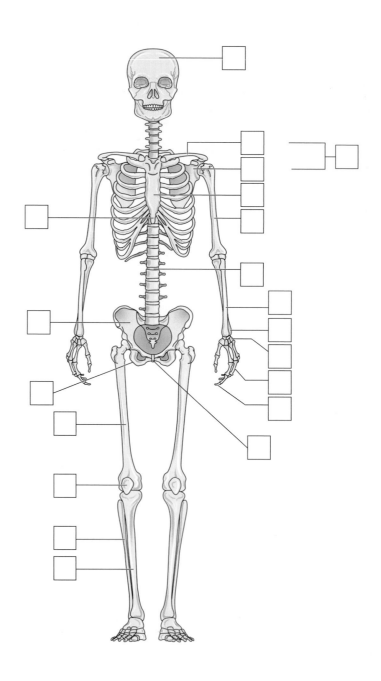

Color the Graphic

Color this illustration using the following color key. Then answer the questions that follow.

frontal – yellow
lacrimal – purple
mandible – brown
maxilla – green

nasal – red
occipital – orange
parietal – light blue
sphenoid – dark blue

styloid – light green
temporal – pink
zygomatic bone – white

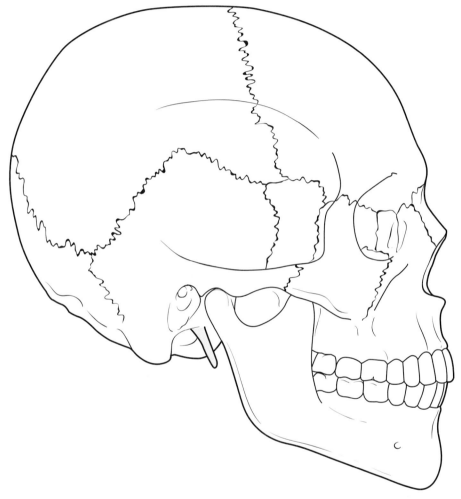

1. Which cranial bone is not shown in this lateral view?

2. Which facial bones cannot be seen in this lateral view?

3. Name three important specialized temporal bone features that are visible in this lateral view.

Additional Practice: The Skeletal System

Identify the location of each of the terms listed above the image. Write the name of the bone on the corresponding line beneath the image.

1. Skull

zygomatic bone	temporal bone	nasal bone
frontal bone	parietal bone	lacrimal bone
maxilla/maxillary bone	mandible	

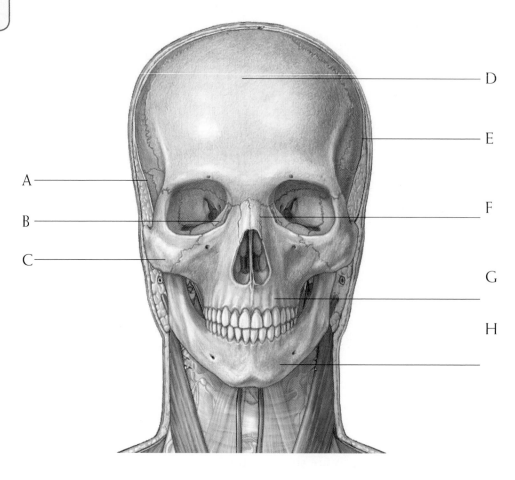

A. _____   E. _____

B. _____   F. _____

C. _____   G. _____

D. _____   H. _____

✿A.D.A.M. Education

2. Skull (Lat) I

occipital bone   parietal bone   zygomatic bone
nasal bone   squamosal suture   lambdoid suture
frontal bone   coronal suture

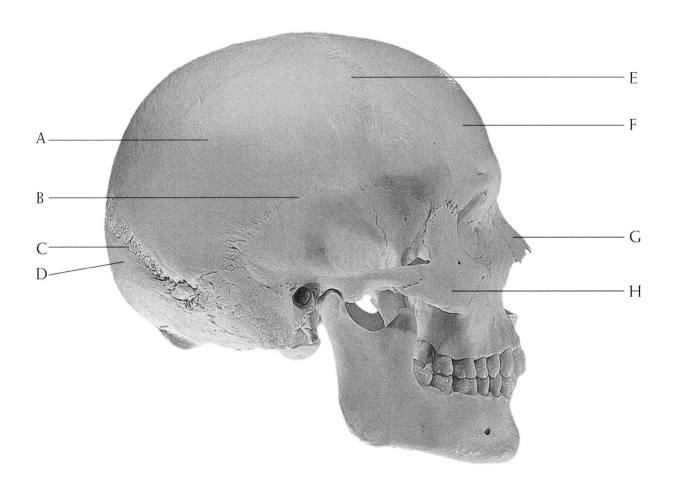

A. _____   E. _____

B. _____   F. _____

C. _____   G. _____

D. _____   H. _____

3. Skull (Lat) II

external acoustic meatus   sutural bone   mastoid process
mandibular condyle   mandible   maxilla / maxillary bone
sphenoid bone

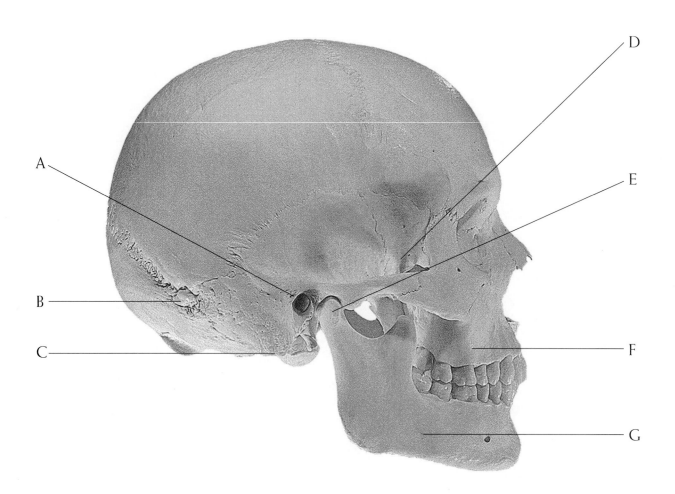

A. _____   E. _____

B. _____   F. _____

C. _____   G. _____

D. _____

4. Cervical vertebrae

dens of C2 (axis) vertebra   C1 (atlas) vertebra
C7 vertebra   1st rib

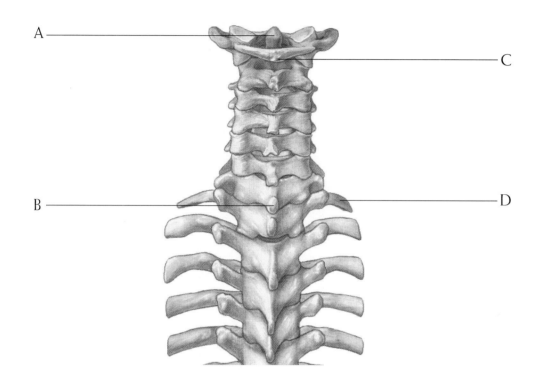

A. _____   C. _____

B. _____   D. _____

5. Bones of Upper Limb

ulna   trochlea of humerus   radius
capitulum of humerus   head of humerus   acromion process of
coracoid process of scapula   clavicle   scapula

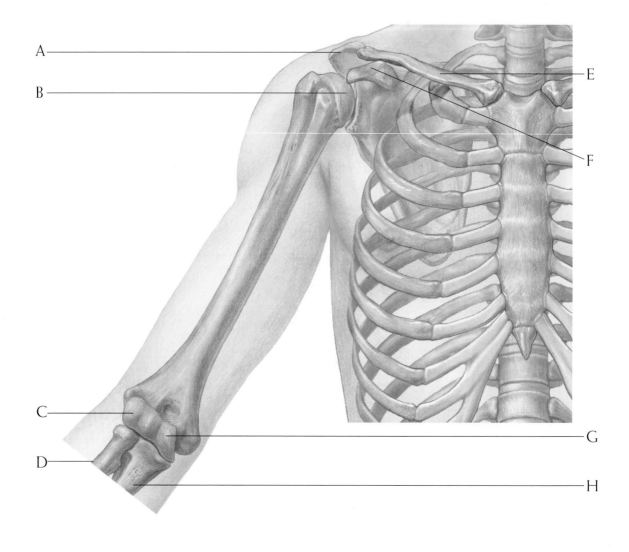

A. _____   E. _____

B. _____   F. _____

C. _____   G. _____

D. _____   H. _____

6. Bones of Hand I

trapezium
scaphoid/navicular
pisiform

lunate
triquetral/triangular
hamate

capitate
trapezoid

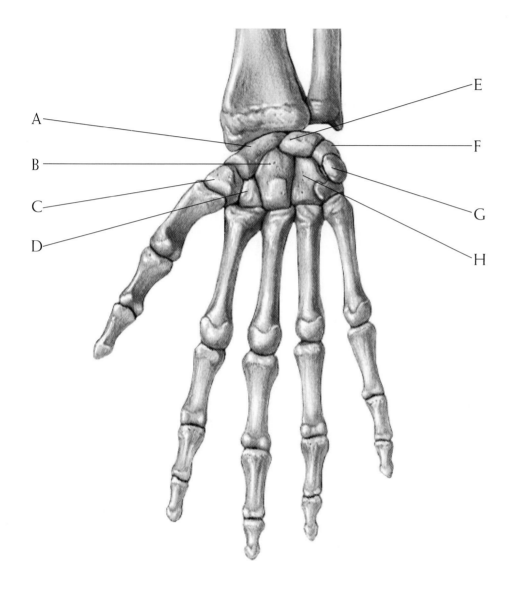

A. _____   E. _____

B. _____   F. _____

C. _____   G. _____

D. _____   H. _____

7. Bones of Hand II

Key Term Reminder Note that the term *phalynx* is synonymous with *phalange*.

1st metacarpal
proximal phalynx of thumb
middle phalynx of finger

2nd metacarpal
distal phalynx of thumb
distal phalynx of finger

5th metacarpal
proximal phalynx
of finger

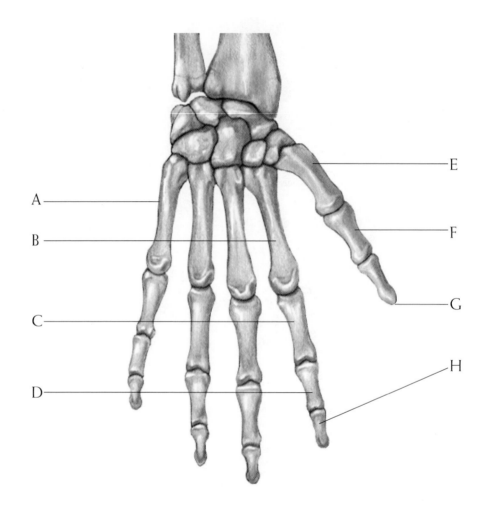

A. _____   E. _____

B. _____   F. _____

C. _____   G. _____

D. _____   H. _____

8. Pelvis and Lower Limb

neck of femur   crest of ilium / ilium   ischium
pubis   head of femur   greater trochanter of femur
lesser trochanter of femur

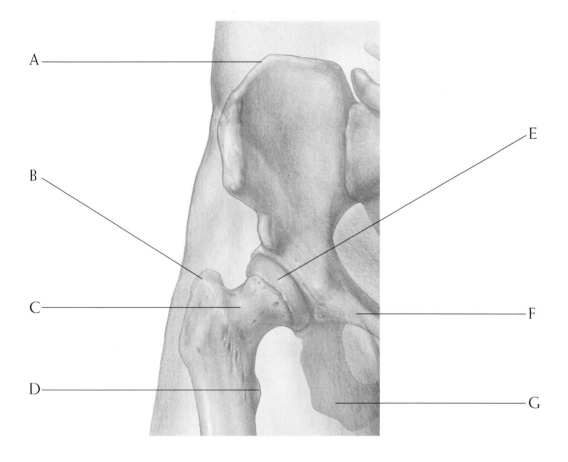

A. _____   E. _____

B. _____   F. _____

C. _____   G. _____

D. _____

9. Bones of Lower Limb

fibula
patella
lateral condyle of tibia

lateral condyle of femur
medial condyle of femur
tuberosity of tibia

shaft of femur
medial condyle of tibia

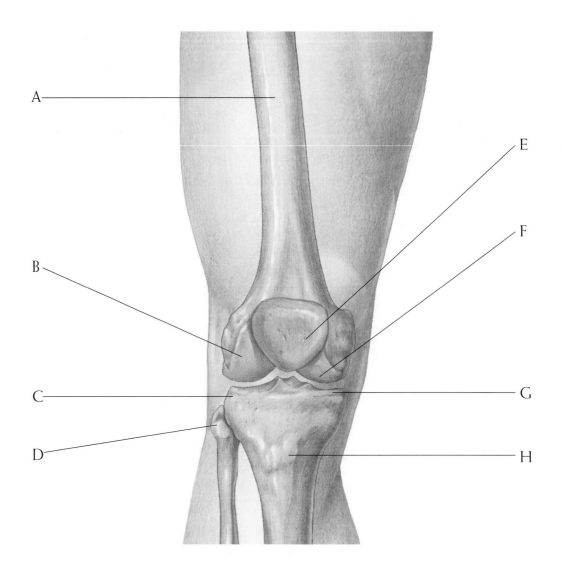

A. _____   E. _____

B. _____   F. _____

C. _____   G. _____

D. _____   H. _____

10. Bones of Foot I

proximal phalanx
proximal phalanx of great toe
second metatarsal

middle phalanx
fifth metatarsal
first metarsal

distal phalanx
fourth metatarsal

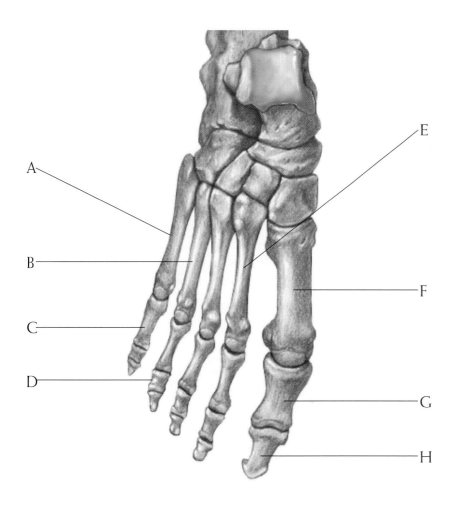

A. _____   E. _____

B. _____   F. _____

C. _____   G. _____

D. _____   H. _____

A.D.A.M. Education

11. Bones of Foot II

calcaneus	talus	navicular
medial (1st) cuneiform	intermediate	lateral (3rd)
cuboid	(2nd) cuneiform	cuneiform

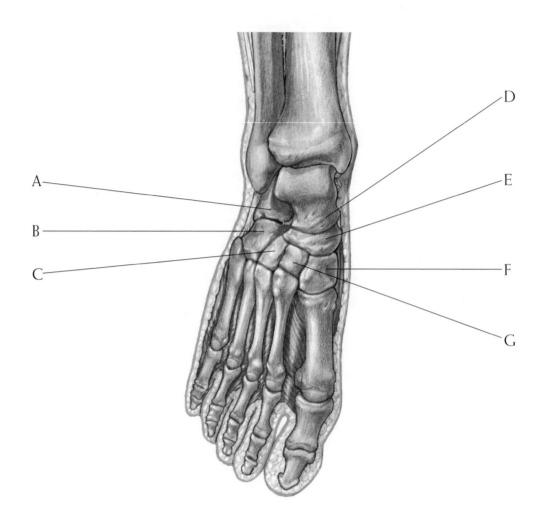

A. _____   E. _____

B. _____   F. _____

C. _____   G. _____

D. _____

Practical Application

Write brief responses to the following scenarios.

1. Describe which bones could be damaged in a "broken nose."

2. Why does a broken clavicle cause restriction of head and arm movement?

3. Many people believe that the name "funny bone" (most often used in reference to the elbow, especially when it is hit against a hard surface) is derived from the name of the upper arm bone. What might be the reason for this word association, and is it really accurate?

4. Which bone in the forearm is located "thumbside"? Is it the lateral or medial of the two forearm bones when the body is in anatomical position? How does its position change in relation to the other bone of the forearm when the hands are in the position opposite of the true anatomical position?

5. Which bones and specific structure form the medial and lateral protrusions felt in the ankle area? Which bone of the foot is articulated with these bones to connect it to the leg?

6. What portions of the hands and feet contain bones with the same name, and what terminology is used to differentiate these bones from one another? Give an example by naming the bone that forms the tip of the thumb and the bone that forms the middle of the middle toe.

7. List two specific areas of the body, and the specific features of each, that would help a forensic pathologist to identify the gender of a person from his or her skeletal remains.

8. When one thinks of the skeletal system, the anatomical arrangement of the bones is usually the predominant feature that comes to mind. What is limiting about this view, in light of the fact that the skeletal system is a true organ system that interacts with other body systems?

9. Can you think of a letter association that might help someone remember the names and respective functions of each of the cell types that begin with the root "osteo" and play a role in endochondrial bone formation?

A.D.A.M. Education

Refer to the Encyclopedia section of A.D.A.M. Interactive Anatomy to open the A.D.A.M. Multimedia Encyclopedia. A quick search of key terms from the textbook will help you reinforce the knowledge you have gained thus far. Try entering pathological terms such as *scleroderma, osteoarthritis, rheumatoid arthritis, lupus,* or *gout* in the search bar to read more about these important topics dealing with the skeletal system.

10. The text defines stress fractures as bone breaks that are too small to heal. Use what you have learned about bone healing to explain why small fractures may not heal.

Laboratory Activity 1

Bone Studies

Background

Bones are helpful in determining how a person lives or lived. Forensic anthropologists study the wear and tear found on bones and joints to provide insight into the lifestyles of long-dead individuals and societies. An anthropologist is a scientist who studies human origins by examining human behavior, physical features, social structures, and cultural development. Anthropology is the study of humans and their ancestors in relation to culture, environmental and social relations, and physical characteristics. Forensic anthropologists use various sciences to answer questions based on the examination and comparison of evidence that gives some information about human origins. Some forensic anthropologists use these strategies and human remains to solve crimes. The remains are what the courts call *biological evidence*. In this activity, you may work with actual human skeletons or casts of real bones to determine certain features of a person using forensic anthropological methods.

Materials

- Entire articulated human skeleton
- Male and female pelvis models
- Prepared slide of thyroid gland
- Ruler with centimeter markings
- Measuring tape with centimeter markings
- Meter stick
- Calculator
- Blackboard or large paper chart to record data
- Computer with Internet access

Procedure

Access the Forensic Anthropology website at http://anatphys.emcp.net/Forensic and click the Human Osteology link to learn how scientists orient and measure human bones for anthropological studies. Is the information consistent with what you learned in this chapter? Next, click the Forensic Anthropology link to see how bone measurement is important in determining features such as age, gender, pathology, race, stature, and trauma. Pair up with a lab partner, and take the following measurements in centimeters on both your partner and the human skeleton, making sure to record your results:

- Total height
- Length of the foot
- Length from the ankle to the hip
- Length from the knee to the ankle or tibia
- Length of the thigh or femur
- Length of the arm, from wrist to shoulder
- Length of the forearm, or radius, from the wrist to the elbow
- Length of the upper arm, or humerus, from the elbow to the shoulder
- Length of the index finger
- Circumference of the wrist
- Circumference of the neck
- Circumference of the leg just above the knee
- Width of outstretched arm span, from fingertip to fingertip
- Width of the back, from shoulder to shoulder

Divide each measurement by the total height of the person to find the bone-to-height ratio. Record your bone-to-height data on the board for class data comparison.

Analysis

Gender Differences Use the information you have found to figure out if there are any skeletal patterns you can use to determine the gender of the person. For example, males have a sloping forehead, while females have a straighter forehead. Plus, the hipbones of males and females show obvious differences, as mentioned in Chapter 5 of the textbook. Males and females may also have different arm and leg bone-to-height ratios. Use this information to answer the following questions:

1. Do all males have the same bone-to-height ratios?

2. Do all females have the same bone-to-height ratios?

3. Besides gender, what other factors can affect bone-to-height ratios?

4. How do the bone-to-height ratios of the skeleton compare with those of the students in class?

Determining Height Forensic anthropologists can use bones to accurately determine the height of a person. For example, it is possible to determine the height of a female just by knowing the length of her femur. The customary way to calculate female height from femur length is to multiply the length of the femur (measured in centimeters) by 1.945 and then add 72.84, as shown in Table 5.1 below. Test the appropriate formula on your lab partner and record the information.

Table 5.1

Base Equation for Females	Factor for Wet Bone (with cartilage)	Factor for Dry Bone (without cartilage)
1.945 x length of femur in cm +	71.163	72.844
2.754 x length of humerus in cm +	70.046	71.475
2.352 x length of tibia in cm +	73.369	74.774
3.343 x length of radius in cm +	80.189	81.224
(1.117 x length of femur in cm) + (1.125 x length of the tibia in cm) +	67.939	69.561
(1.339 x length of femur in cm) + (1.027 x length of humerus in cm) +	65.763	67.435
Base Equation for Males	**Factor for Wet Bone (with cartilage)**	**Factor for Dry Bone (without cartilage)**
1.88 x length of femur in cm +	79.971	81.306
2.894 x length of humerus in cm +	69.454	70.641
2.376 x length of tibia in cm +	77.547	78.664
3.271 x length of radius in cm +	85.205	85.925
(1.22 x length of femur in cm) + (1.080 x length of the tibia in cm) +	70.069	71.443
(1.03 x length of femur in cm) + (1.557 x length of humerus in cm) +	67.027	68.397

Laboratory Activity 2

Comparative Anatomy of Primates

Background

It might be surprising to learn that physicians are now using comparative anatomy (the comparison of features and structures between different species) to better understand dental and skeletal abnormalities in humans. Primates are particularly important in these studies because of their close kinship to humans. Scientists compare human bones that contain defects due to mutations in bone-development genes by visually comparing them with primate bones and recording their differences and similarities. They then try to determine whether any of the mutations in human bones match up with normal growth patterns found in primates and other animals. Scientists hope that determining whether a mutation causes changes that resemble the normal growth of other animals will help to give them a better understanding of how the mutation occurs.

Materials

- Computer with Internet access
- Disarticulated human skeleton with skull

Procedure

Access the eSkeletons Project website at http://anatphys.emcp.net/eSkeletons. Go to the Select the Taxon drop-down menu, and review the different bones of the human and the primates. Note that the different body regions are colored to indicate similar structures. Next, click the Comparative Anatomy link. Select the various bones to compare the human and primate versions side-by-side.

Analysis

Use what you observed on the eSkeletons Project website to answer the following questions:

1. What are the major differences in dentition between humans and the other primates?

2. What are three main differences between the human skull and the skulls of the other primates?

3. What explains the differences between the human and gorilla tibia?

4. How do the calcaneus bones differ in each of the specimens, and what about the specimens' ways of life might explain the differences?

5. How do the thoracic vertebrae differ between the specimens? What human conditions can explain how vertebrae resemble those of the other primates?

1. Which of the following is true of the axial skeleton?
    a) It includes the arms and legs.
    b) It forms a horizontal axis in the body.
    c) It is composed of the skull, ribs, and vertebrae.
    d) It is the division of the skeleton that contains the largest number of bones.

2. Which of the following cranial bones does *not* form the calvaria?
    a) parietal
    b) temporal
    c) ethmoid
    d) frontal

3. Which of the following facial bones does *not* form a part of the nasal cavity?
    a) ethmoid
    b) zygomatic
    c) vomer
    d) inferior conchae

4. Which of the following is *not* a bone that forms the orbit?
    a) lacrimal
    b) sphenoid
    c) ethmoid
    d) occipital

5. Foramens, processes, tubercles, and facets are all examples of:
    a) articulations
    b) surface features
    c) joints
    d) All of the above

6. On the basis of their embryological development, most of the facial bones, as well as the arm and leg bones, are classified as:
    a) alveolar
    b) dermal
    c) cancellous
    d) endoskeletal

7. Which of the following is true of a long bone?
    a) The shaft or main body is called the epiphysis.
    b) Each end terminates in a region called the diaphysis.
    c) The diaphysis grows in opposite directions to elongate the bone.
    d) All of the above

8. Bone matrix is composed of:
    a) osteocalcin
    b) hydroxylapatite
    c) collagen fiber
    d) All of the above

9. Compact, or cortical, bone:
   a) makes up about 80% of the bones in the human body
   b) is composed of microscopic structural units called osteons
   c) contributes only a small proportion of bone weight
   d) forms the ends of long bones and the center of other bones

10. Which of the following best describes synovial fluid?
   a) It is found in bursa.
   b) It lubricates joint linings.
   c) It is found in synovial capsules.
   d) All of the above

11. Which of the following is the correct order in the process of endochondrial bone formation?
   a) bone collar formation, cartilage peg formation, epiphysial osteoclast activity
   b) cartilage peg formation, bone collar formation, epiphsial osteoclast activity
   c) epiphysial osteoclast activity, bone collar formation, secondary ossification
   d) osteoclast activity at cartilage pegs, secondary ossification, bone collar formation

12. The five stages of endochondrial bone formation can be condensed into three phases known as:
   a) reactive, reparative, and restorative
   b) initiating, rebuilding, and molding
   c) reaction, repair, and shaping
   d) response, resourcing, and restoration

13. Shin splints:
   a) are a type of stress fracture
   b) involve the bone tissue of the tibia
   c) result from abnormal stretching of the ligaments and tendons
   d) All of the above

14. Tooth decay includes:
   a) loss of calcium from teeth
   b) formation of cavities
   c) loss of collagen connective tissue
   d) All of the above

15. Myeloma is cancer of:
   a) red blood cells
   b) red bone marrow
   c) bone cells
   d) white blood cells

16. Which of the following skeletal system conditions is due to loss of blood flow?
   a) osteonecrosis
   b) scleroderma
   c) osteomyelitis
   d) osteomalacia

17. Match the letter of each type of joint with the best description of the movement it allows:

a) amphiarthrosis   _____ widest variety of movements

b) diarthrosis   _____ only slight movement

c) synarthrosis   _____ no movement

18. Match the letter of each type of synarthrosis with the corresponding description:

a) gomphosis   _____ ligaments

b) synchondrosis   _____ bone fusion

c) syndesmosis   _____ cartilage

d) synostosis   _____ socket

19. Match the letter of each type of bone fracture with the corresponding description:

a) comminuted (compound)   _____ skin tearing

b) greenstick   _____ bone displacement

c) open   _____ very small

d) simple   _____ break and bend of bone

e) stress   _____ cracked bone only

20. Match the letter of each type of arthritis with the corresponding description:

a) ankylosing spondylitis   _____ affects cartilage at bone ends

b) rheumatoid arthritis   _____ affects spine articular cartilage

c) osteoarthritis   _____ autoimmune attack of connective tissue

21. For each bone shape, list the type of ossification that usually occurs during its development:

a) long bones

b) flat bones

c) irregular

22. List five categories of synovial joints (based on the motion permitted by each), and name two bones that are articulated by each category.

   a)

   b)

   c)

   d)

   e)

23. Place the following stages of bone healing in the order of occurrence from beginning to end: callus, granulation, lamellar bone, fracture, and normal contour.

24. List three factors that are thought to contribute to osteoporosis.

25. List four factors that can contribute to aging of the skeletal system.

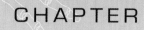

CHAPTER

THE MUSCULAR SYSTEM

Introduction

The muscular system makes up over half of the body's mass, and it consumes a large amount of the energy obtained through the diet. Muscles are categorized into three distinct types: skeletal, smooth, and cardiac. The majority of muscle in the body is skeletal muscle, which is responsible for the movement of the skeletal frame. Smooth muscle is found within the walls of most hollow organs, and is responsible for moving substances within the body (such as the passage of food and waste through the digestive system). Cardiac muscle is found only in the heart, and contains specialized cells that contract as a unit to pump blood throughout the body. The following exercises and lab activities will help you apply what you have learned about the structure and function of the muscular system. If you need assistance, refer to Chapter 6 of *Applied Anatomy & Physiology, A Case Study Approach*. Additionally, you can access A.D.A.M. Interactive Anatomy for information that will expand your understanding of the concepts presented in the textbook.

Completion

Complete the following sentences by filling in each blank with a key term from the text.

1. Muscle cells can be classified three ways: 1) _____, 2) type of _____, and 3) _____.

2. The contractile unit of a muscle cell is called a _____, which is composed of an overlapping pattern of thick and thin _____.

3. Skeletal muscle contraction is initiated by the nerve cell release of the neurotransmitter _____, which binds to a _____ on the muscle cell's membrane, or _____.

4. A resting muscle cell normally has a higher intracellular ion concentration of _____ and a higher extracellular concentration of _____. These levels are maintained by a system called the _____ _____.

5. Skeletal muscle contraction occurs in three stages: 1) _____, 2) _____, and 3) _____.

6. The immovable muscle attachment point is called the _____, and the connection to the body part that moves during a muscle contraction is called the _____.

7. The three levels of muscle structure are 1) _____, 2) _____, and 3) _____.

8. _____ describes a muscle action of active lengthening or shortening, while _____ describes action with no change in muscle length.

9. _____ muscle fibers are referred to as *white* because they contain only small amounts of _____. They are referred to metabolically as _____ because they undergo _____ respiration.

10. _____ muscle fibers are referred to as *red* because they contain large amounts of _____. They are referred to metabolically as _____ because they undergo _____ respiration.

Matching

Match each of the following terms with the corresponding description by placing the letter of the term on the blank next to the correct description.

a) antagonistic

b) cachexia

c) cardiac muscle

d) contractile proteins

e) creatine phosphate

f) fascicle

g) motor

h) myoglobin

i) neuromuscular junction

j) nonstriated

k) sarcolemma

l) smooth muscle

m) sphincter

n) sprain

o) type II fibers

_____ random pattern of contractile proteins

_____ found in digestive organs and bloodvessels

_____ nerves that control skeletal muscle

_____ intrinsic beat

_____ muscle cell membrane

_____ space between a nerve cell and sarcolemma

_____ stores energy in muscle cells

_____ a bundle of muscle fibers

_____ muscle action that resists another muscle

_____ decrease in the size of an opening

_____ fast glycolytic

_____ type of muscle injury

_____ muscle loss

_____ stores oxygen for aerobic respiration of muscle

_____ causes muscle cell cytoskeleton to contract

Complete the Terms Table

Fill in the missing key terms and/or definitions in the following table.

Term	Definition
	embryological development of muscle tissue from mesoderm cells
myofilaments	
myofibrils	
	the system of the inner membrane of muscle cells that stores and transports calcium for muscle contraction
rigor mortis	
	the stable, immovable point of attachment of a muscle
	connective tissue covering gross muscle
synergistic	
rotator	
	a muscle fiber type also known as slow oxidative due to its metabolic activity of aerobic respiration
	abnormal involuntary muscle movement
cramp	
myopathy	
	a calcium imbalance disease that causes arm and leg spasms
muscular dystrophies	

Label the Graphic

Identify each of the following in the illustrations on pages 85 and 86. Write the number of the anatomical part in the box indicating its location.

1. biceps brachii (arm)
2. biceps femoris (thigh)
3. deltoid muscle
4. frontal muscle
5. gastrocnemius
6. gluteal muscles
7. gracilis muscle
8. latissimus dorsi
9. occipital muscle
10. orbicularis oculi (eye)
11. orbicularis oris (mouth)
12. pectoral muscle
13. quadriceps muscle
14. rectus abdominis
15. sartorius muscle
16. semimembranous muscle
17. semitendinosus muscle
18. splenius muscle
19. sternocleidomastoid muscle
20. temporal muscle
21. teres muscles
22. anterior tibial muscle
23. trapezius muscle
24. triceps brachii (arm)

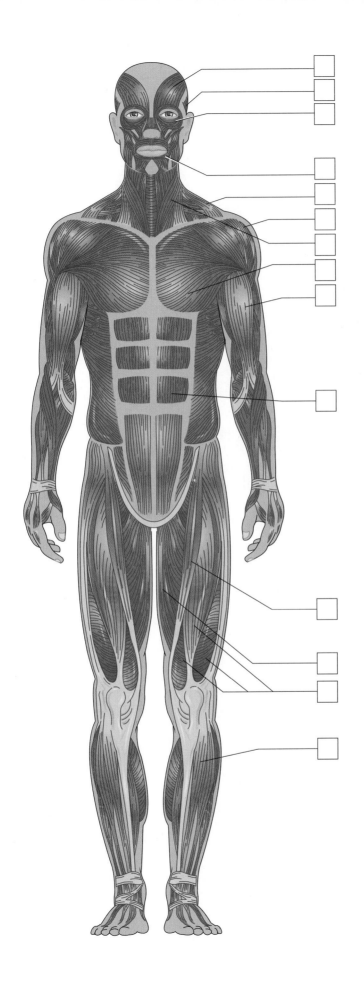

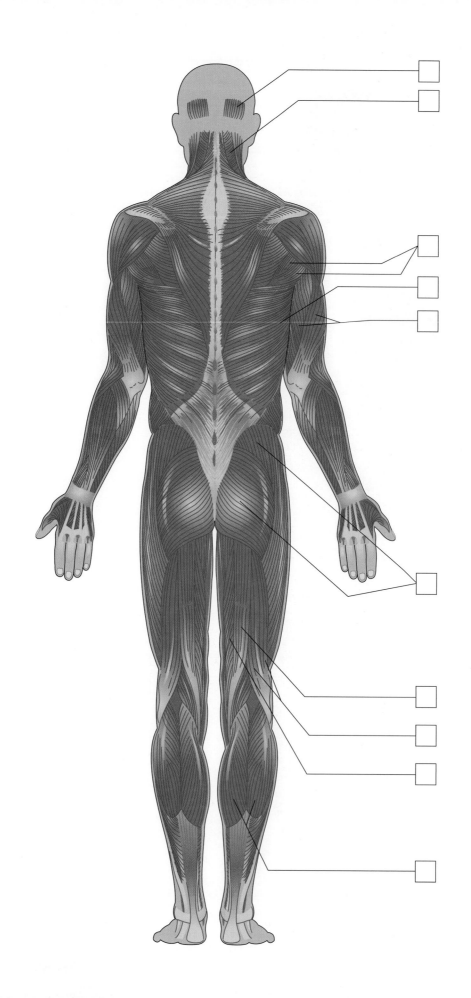

Color the Graphic

Color this illustration using the following color key:

muscle – pink
tendon – brown
fasciculi – red
muscle fiber – orange
single myofibril – purple

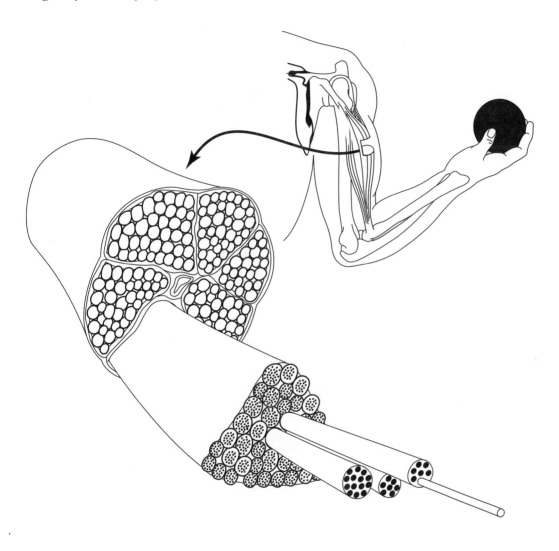

Additional Practice: The Muscular System

Identify the location of each of the terms listed above the image. Write the name of the muscle on the corresponding line beneath the image.

1. Face Muscles

frontalis (frontal) muscle
orbicularis oculi muscle / orbicular
   muscle of eye
trapezius

sternocleidomastoid muscle
levator labii superioris muscle
orbicularis oris muscle

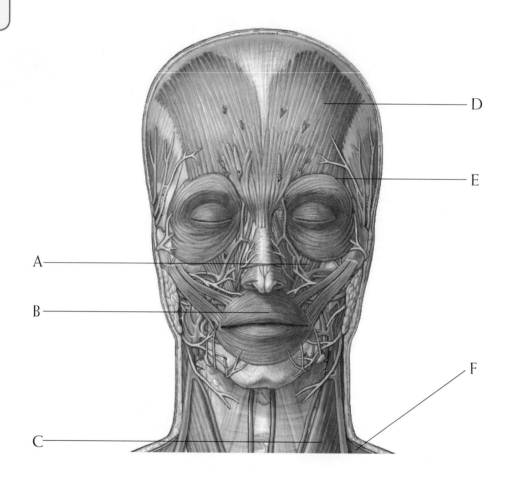

A. _____ D. _____

B. _____ E. _____

C. _____ F. _____

2. Face Muscles (Lat)

occipitalis / occiptal
   muscle
frontalis / frontal muscle
masseter muscle

parotid gland
orbicularis oculi muscle
   / orbicular muscle of
   the eye

sternocleidomastoid
   muscle
orbicularis oris muscle
   / orbicular muscle of
   the mouth

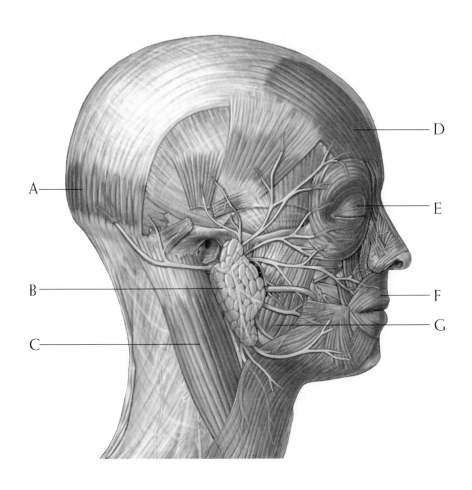

A. _____

B. _____

C. _____

D. _____

E. _____

F. _____

G. _____

3. Shoulder and Arm Muscles (Post)

infraspinatus muscle /
infraspinous muscle
long head of triceps
brachi muscle
rhomboid minor muscle

teres minor muscle
lateral head of triceps
brachii muscle
rhomboid major muscle

teres major muscle
supraspinatus muscle /
supraspinous muscle

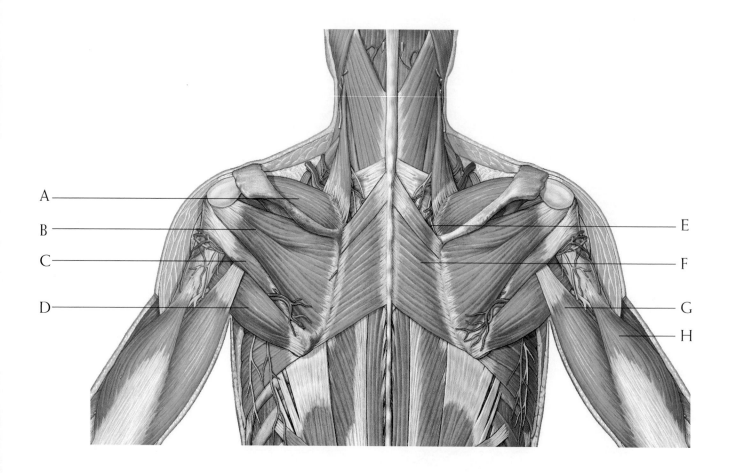

A. _____   E. _____

B. _____   F. _____

C. _____   G. _____

D. _____   H. _____

4. Forearm Muscles

bicep brachii muscle / biceps muscle of arm

pronator teres muscle

brachialis muscle / brachial muscle

flexor carpi radialis muscle / radial flexor muscle of wrist

flexor carpi ulnaris muscle / ulnar flexor muscle of wrist

brachioradialis muscle / brachioradial muscle

A. _____   D. _____

B. _____   E. _____

C. _____   F. _____

5. Thorax Muscles

sternocleidomastoid muscle
external oblique muscle
pectoralis major muscle / greater
    pectoral muscle

trapezius muscle
deltoid muscle
serratus anterior muscle / anterior
    serratus muscle

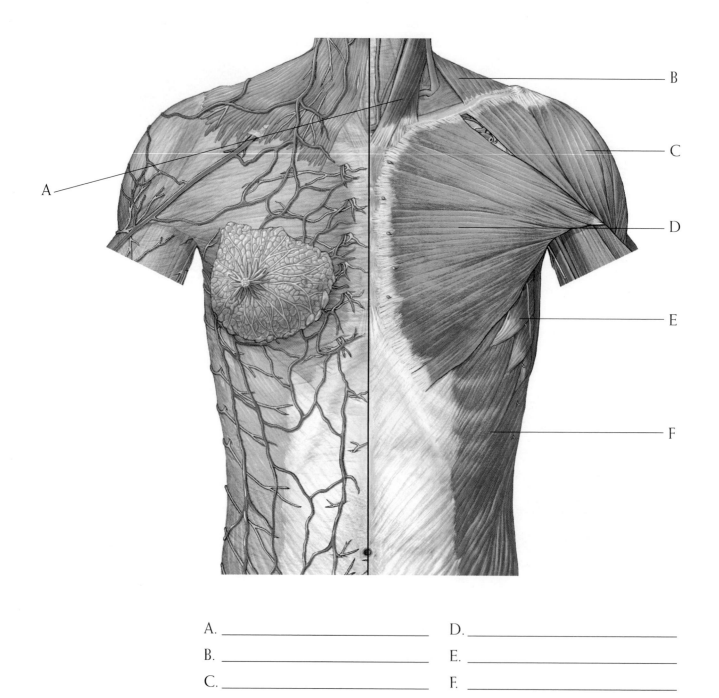

A. _____   D. _____

B. _____   E. _____

C. _____   F. _____

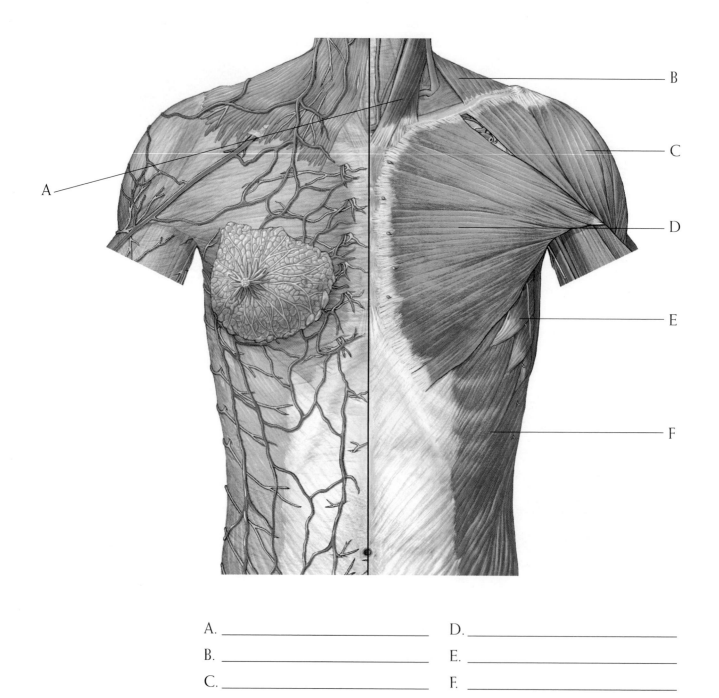 *A.D.A.M.* Education

6. Shoulder and Arm Muscles

deltoid muscle
serratus anterior muscle / anterior
   serratus muscle
lateral head of triceps brachii muscle

coracobrachialis muscle
brachialis muscle / brachial muscle
long head of triceps brachi muscle

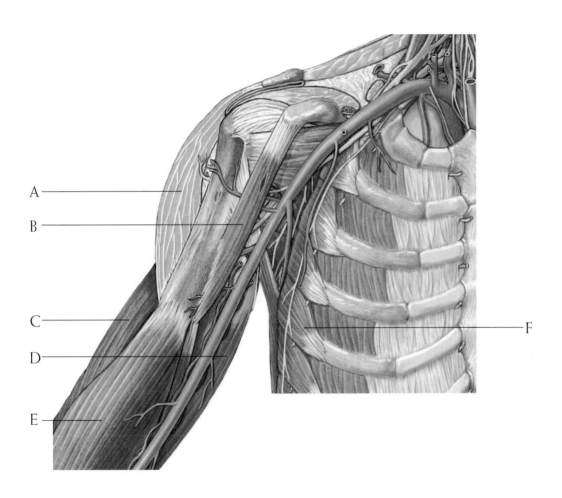

A. _____   D. _____

B. _____   E. _____

C. _____   F. _____

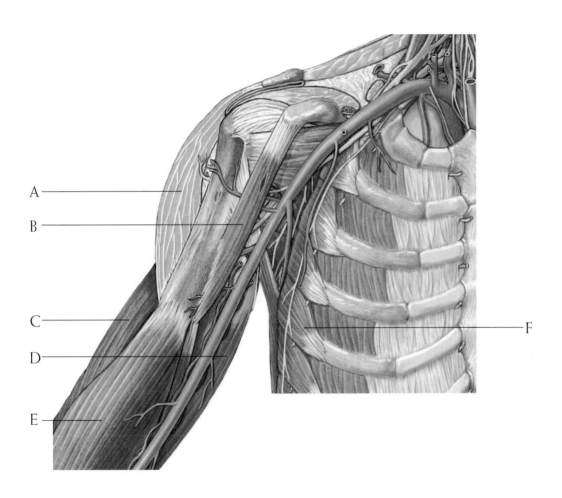

7. Thigh Muscles

tensor fasciae latae muscle
vastus medialis muscle
adductor magnus muscle /
 great adductor muscle

rectus femoris muscle
pectineus muscle
sartorius muscle

vastus lateralis muscle
adductor longus muscle

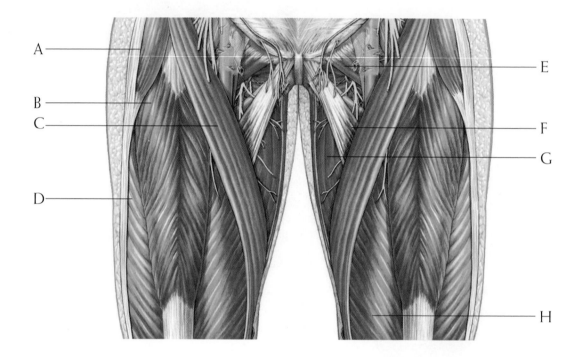

A. _____   E. _____

B. _____   F. _____

C. _____   G. _____

D. _____   H. _____

8. Pelvis and Thigh Muscles (Med)

rectus femoris muscle
adductor magnus muscle /
   great adductor muscle
semimembranosus muscle

vastus medialis muscle
gracilis muscle
sartorius muscle

adductor longus muscle
semitendinosus muscle

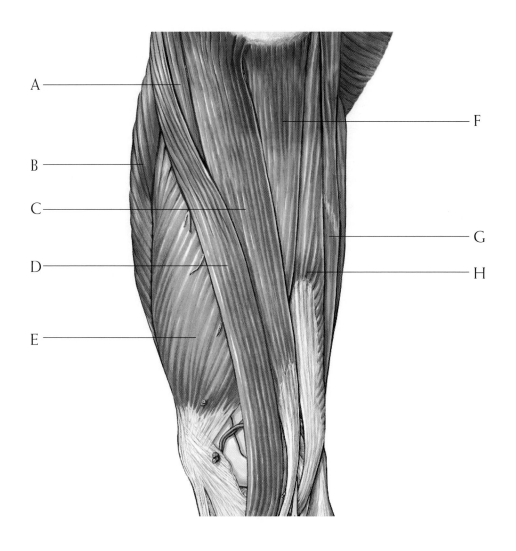

A. _____   E. _____

B. _____   F. _____

C. _____   G. _____

D. _____   H. _____

*A.D.A.M. Education

9. Hip and Thigh Muscles (Post)

gluteus maximus muscle   vastus lateralis muscle   biceps femoris muscle
semitendinosus muscle   iliotibial tract / ligament   adductor magnus
gracilis muscle   semimembranosus   muscle / great
    muscle   adductor muscle

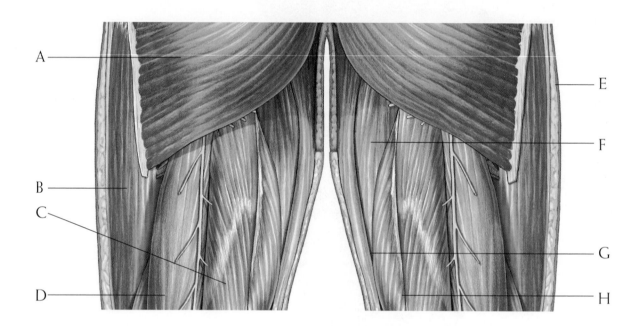

A. _____   E. _____

B. _____   F. _____

C. _____   G. _____

D. _____   H. _____

Write brief responses to the following scenarios.

1. How would stimulation of smooth muscle contraction affect blood pressure, air inhalation, and defecation (i.e., evacuation of food waste from the digestive tract)?

2. Sympathetic nerve activity is usually associated with the phrase "fight or flight." This often leads to the misconception that sympathetic nerve activity is only excitatory in nature. Explain why this is inaccurate.

3. An enzyme called acetylcholinesterase breaks down acetylcholine at the neuromuscular synapse. Would an anticholinesterase drug (an inhibitor of this enzyme) cause an increase or decrease in skeletal muscle activity? Would this effect be described as blocking or increasing sympathetic nerve activity?

4. What are the two major antagonistic muscle groups located proximally on the lower appendages? (Use Figures 6.10a and 6.10b as a reference.) Identify their locations and actions, and explain which attachment points they might have in common. Describe why the contraction of each muscle results in the identified action (include the terms *origin* and *insertion* in your answer).

5. Why is skeletal muscle multinucleated?

6. When the diaphragm muscle contracts, its position in the body is lowered. In contrast, when the external intercostal muscles of the ribs contract, they become elevated. Both of these muscle contractions create more volume in the thoracic cavity. The resultant decrease in the pressure within the thoracic cavity causes air to move from the body's exterior (where there is higher pressure) into the lower-pressure area of the thoracic cavity. Thus, inspiration occurs as the lungs fill with air. Relaxing of these muscles returns them to their original positions, and exhaling forces air out. Given this information about the mechanics of inspiration, how might the calcium leakage into the sarcomeres of diaphragm muscle tissue that occurs following death help to explain the phenomenon of a corpse making a "moaning" sound?

7. The deltoid muscle "caps" the shoulder. Its origin is on the bones of the shoulder girdle, and its insertion is on the deltoid tuberosity, located on the lateral side of the humerus. Based on this information, which term of muscle movement best describes the action of the deltoid muscle? Explain how this action occurs. Which muscle movement term describes the action of muscles antagonistic to the deltoid?

8. Do you think the muscles that cause flexion of the neck have their origin or their insertion on the head? Explain your reasoning.

🌸A.D.A.M.Education

Click on the Encyclopedia tab in A.D.A.M. Interactive Anatomy to open the A.D.A.M. Multimedia Encyclopedia. A quick search of key terms from the textbook will help you reinforce the knowledge you have gained thus far. Try entering pathological terms such as *sprain*, *strain*, *paralysis*, *tetany*, or *muscular dystrophy* in the search bar to read more about these important topics dealing with the muscular system.

9. Classify each of the following activities as either isometric or isotonic, and briefly explain your answers: 1) biceps curls; and 2) balancing on tip toes.

10. Describe the condition *myolitis ossificans* by breaking down the meaning of the "subparts" of the words.

Laboratory Activity 1

Effect of Ambient Temperature on Muscle Action

Background

The body's organ systems work together to maintain consistent conditions that resist changes in the surrounding environment. However, superficial organs and tissues, such as the smaller surface muscles, cannot always adapt accordingly. Sometimes their cellular environments fluctuate with changes in the surrounding, or ambient, conditions. People who work outdoors, or in extremely cold or hot environments, must be aware of the limitations these conditions impose on the body. In this activity, you will investigate the effects of ambient temperature on superficial muscle action.

Materials

- Lab partner
- Clock with a second hand, or a stopwatch
- Two small buckets
- Two thermometers
- Access to warm water (40°C or 104°F)
- Access to cold water (to be chilled with ice to 3°C or 5°C)
- Access to ice

Procedure

Follow the steps below to investigate the effects of temperature on muscle action:

1. Select a person to be the experimental subject. Make sure the subject is able to make a fist repeatedly without feeling any pain or resistance to his or her hand movement.
2. Set out the buckets of ice water and warm water.
3. Record the room temperature.
4. Prepare to start timing the subject while he or she makes repeated fists with one hand.
5. First, count the number of times the subject can make a fist in 20 seconds. Start timing when the hand is completely outstretched. The subject should try to make as tight a fist as possible, as fast as possible, each time. Record the count in Table 6.1 on the next page. Repeat this step five times. Calculate the average, and record it in the table.
6. Next, have the subject submerge the same hand in the bucket of warm water. Keep the hand in the water for 2 minutes.
7. Now, have the subject remove his or her hand and immediately start making fists again. Count how many fists he or she can make in 20 seconds. Record the data in Table 16.1. Repeat this step five times. Calculate the average and record that as well.
8. Have the subject submerge the same hand in the bucket of cold water chilled with ice. Keep the hand in the water for 2 minutes.
9. Now, have the subject remove the hand and immediately start making fists again. Count how many fists he or she can make in 20 seconds. Record the data in Table 6.1. Repeat this step five times. Calculate the average, and record that as well.

Table 6.1 Activity 1 Data

Temperature	Number of Fists/ 20 sec					Average
room temperature (_____°C or _____°F)						
warm water						
cold water						

Analysis

1. Write an analytical statement that describes what you can conclude from your data.
2. How can any differences in the rate of fist clenching be explained?
3. How might these findings be useful for people who exercise or work outdoors? Describe a few scenarios in which this information would be helpful to know.

Laboratory Activity 2

Effect of Fatigue on Grip Muscle Action

Background

Muscle fatigue occurs after extended or strong muscle contractions. Research shows that short-term muscle fatigue is associated with a lack of oxygen and subsequent buildup of lactic acid in the muscle. Long-term muscle fatigue is related to the rate of glycogen reduction. As discussed in this chapter, muscle cell fatigue is based on the muscle's ability to provide energy for contraction. Some muscles fatigue after short bursts of activity, while others fatigue only after prolonged action. Each person has a unique muscle composition and structure that determine the rate at which a muscle group fatigues during a particular activity. In this activity, you will investigate whether there are any differences in how muscle fatigue affects the muscle action of two people.

Materials

- Two lab partners to act in the roles of Subject 1 and Subject 2
- Two tennis balls
- Clock with a second hand, or a stopwatch
- Measuring tape
- Red pen or pencil
- Blue pen or pencil

Procedure

Follow the steps below to investigate the effects of fatigue on muscle action:

1. Label your research subjects Subject 1 and Subject 2. Using the measuring tape, measure the length, width, and circumference of the hand that each subject will use to squeeze the tennis ball. Also measure the length of the arm from the elbow to the wrist, as well as the diameter of the wrist. Record the data in Table 6.2.
2. Count how many times Subject 1 can tightly squeeze a tennis ball in 30 seconds. Record the number in Table 6.3.

3. Immediately repeat step 2 nine more times, and record the data in Table 6.3. The subject should not be able to rest between each trial.
4. Immediately after the trials, use the measuring tape to measure the length, width, and circumference of the hand that Subject 1 used to squeeze the tennis ball. Again, measure the length of the arm from elbow to wrist, as well as the diameter of the wrist. Record the data in Table 6.2.
5. Repeat steps 2–4 for Subject 2.
6. After completing the trials with both subjects, make a line graph with the data from Table 6.3 in Figure 6.1 on the next page. Use the red pen for Subject 1 and the blue pen for Subject 2.

Table 6.2 Subject's Dimensions

Measurement	Subject 1		Subject 2	
	Before	After	Before	After
hand length				
hand width				
hand circumference				
forearm length				
wrist circumference				

Table 6.3 Grip Fatigue Chart

Trial	Number of Squeezes per 30 Seconds	
	Subject 1	Subject 2
1.		
2.		
3.		
4.		
5.		
6.		
7.		
8.		
9.		
10.		

Figure 6.1 Effect of Fatigue on Grip Muscle Action Graph

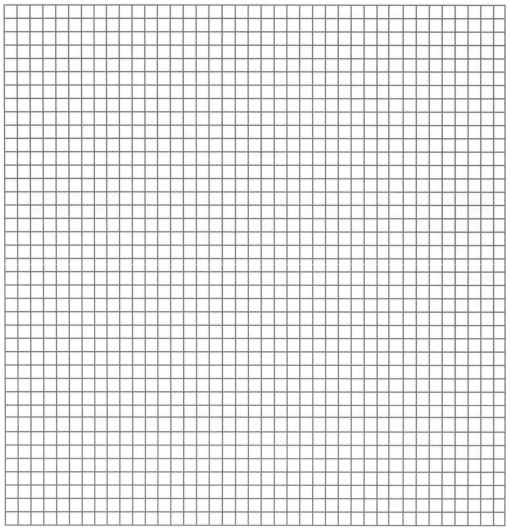

Analysis

1. What muscle changes did you observe while the muscle was working (contracted)?
2. As the trials progressed, what happened to the number of squeezes each subject was able to complete in 30 seconds?
3. Where on the graph does it appear that muscle fatigue set in for each subject on grip action? Explain why you picked that point.
4. Were there any differences between the graphs of the two subjects? If so, what could explain these differences?
5. Is there a relationship between the arm and hand measurements and the point of fatigue?

1. Striations are produced by the uniform arrangement of:
   a) muscle fibers
   b) ion channels
   c) acetylcholine
   d) All of the above

2. Over _____ percent of the body's mass is composed of muscle tissue.
   a) 25
   b) 10
   c) 75
   d) 50

3. Muscles can be categorized as:
   a) striated and nonstriated
   b) involuntary and voluntary
   c) cardiac, skeletal, and smooth
   d) All of the above

4. When a muscle cell is contracted, microscopic observation would reveal:
   a) the overlap of thick and thin filaments
   b) an increased distance between the Z lines
   c) a lack of striations
   d) All of the above

5. The three proteins in thin myofilaments are:
   a) myosin, titin, and actin
   b) tropomyosin, troponin, and myosin
   c) actin, tropomyosin, and troponin
   d) titin, myosin, and tropomyosin

6. Muscle cell contraction is initiated by nerve cell release of:
   a) epinephrine
   b) troponin
   c) calcium
   d) acetylcholine

7. The muscle cell contraction phase begins when the sarcoplasmic reticulum releases _____, which binds to the protein _____ on the thin myofilaments.
   a) acetylcholine/receptors
   b) calcium/troponin
   c) potassium/myosin
   d) sodium/ion channels

8. During muscle cell relaxation:
   a) there is no continued neural stimulation of the sarcolemma
   b) calcium is released
   c) special neurotransmitters are released to lengthen muscles
   d) All of the above

9. The Z line of the sarcomere:
   a) connects the thick and thin filaments
   b) anchors the sarcomeres to the sarcolemma
   c) forms the sarcoplasmic reticulum
   d) All of the above

10. Which of the following correctly lists the terms of muscle anatomy in order from smallest to largest?
    a) myofilament, myofibril, muscle fiber, fascicle
    b) myofibril, myofilament, fascicle, muscle fiber
    c) fascicle, myofilament, myofibril, muscle fiber
    d) muscle fiber, fascicle, myofibril, myofilament

11. Which of the following is involved in energy storage for muscle contraction?
    a) creatine phosphate
    b) glycogen
    c) myoglobin
    d) All of the above

12. When a muscle contracts, the insertion:
    a) remains stationary
    b) moves toward the origin
    c) detaches
    d) has no functional role

13. Type II fibers:
    a) fatigue easily
    b) undergo anaerobic respiration
    c) create lactic acid
    d) All of the above

14. Isotonic muscle action involves:
    a) only muscles of the appendages
    b) active lengthening and shortening
    c) isolation of muscle fibers
    d) All of the above

15. Type I fibers:
    a) undergo aerobic respiration
    b) are white
    c) have small amounts of myoglobin
    d) All of the above

16. Type II fibers:
    a) undergo aerobic respiration
    b) have large amounts of myoglobin
    c) are abundant in muscles used for activities like sprinting
    d) All of the above

17. Mitochondrial myopathies prevent muscle cells from producing:
    a) glucose
    b) oxygen
    c) energy
    d) creatine phosphate

18. Muscular dystrophies:
    a) result in muscle atrophy
    b) usually result from inadequate innervation
    c) are characterized by progressive muscle wasting
    d) All of the above

19. Match the letter of each of the gross-muscle shapes with the corresponding description.
    a) rhomboideus _____ saw toothed
    b) serratus   _____ diamond shaped
    c) trapezius   _____ triangular

20. Match each of the following types of muscle action with the corresponding description.
    a) abductor   _____ produces a downward movement
    b) depressor _____ turns the palm downward
    c) flexor   _____ decreases the angle of a joint
    d) pronator   _____ moves a body part away from the midline

21. Match each of the following types of muscle action with its antagonist.
    a) abductor   _____ levator
    b) depressor _____ supinator
    c) flexor   _____ adductor
    d) pronator   _____ extensor

22. List three aging factors that contribute to cachexia.

23. List the three types of connective tissue within the skeletal muscle structure along with the structures they cover.

24. List the three types of muscle tissue that are classified by their location in the body.

25. Differentiate between rigid and flaccid paralysis.

CHAPTER

7 THE ENDOCRINE GLANDS AND HORMONES

Introduction

The endocrine system plays a vital role in the maintenance of homeostasis in the body. It is composed of several glands and millions of specialized cells that produce secretions known as hormones. These hormones are carried throughout the bloodstream and bind to receptors on target cells, causing the cells to alter their metabolism. Small changes in hormone secretions can cause significant alterations in body function. The following exercises and lab activities will require you to apply what you have learned about the endocrine system and its hormones. If you need assistance, refer to Chapter 7 of *Applied Anatomy & Physiology, A Case Study Approach*. Additionally, you can access A.D.A.M. Interactive Anatomy for information that will expand your understanding of the concepts presented in the textbook.

Completion

Complete the following sentences by filling in each blank with a key term from the text.

1. Secretions that circulate to their target organ are produced by _____ glands while secretions that enter a body area through a duct are produced by _____ glands.

2. Some hormones reach _____ receptors via transport by carrier proteins.

3. Most _____ hormones attach to external receptors, but _____ hormones dissolve across the cell membrane and bind to receptors inside the cell.

4. Nerve cells of the hypothalamus produce chemicals called _____, which travel to the _____ _____ gland to stimulate the production of hormones.

5. _____ decreases blood calcium levels, while _____ _____ increases blood calcium levels.

107

6. _____ cells of the pancreas produce _____, which lowers blood glucose levels, while _____ cells of the pancreas produce _____, which raises blood glucose levels.

7. The pineal gland produces both _____, a hormone involved in digestion, emotion, and sleep, and _____, a hormone that regulates body rhythms and is stimulated by sunlight.

8. The cortex of the adrenal gland produces two major groups of hormones called _____ and _____, while the adrenal medulla produces _____ and _____.

9. An abnormally low level of adrenal cortex hormone production can result in _____ disease, while overproduction of these hormones is the cause of _____ _____.

10. The hormone most commonly involved in hormone replacement therapy is _____; its presence in _____ makes this food a natural alternative sought by many to counteract diminished production of the hormone during the _____ process.

Matching

Match each of the following terms with the corresponding description by writing the letter of the term on the blank next to the correct description.

a) aldosterone

b) antagonist

c) autocrine

d) cortisol

e) diabetes insipidus

f) follicle-stimulating hormone

g) Graves' disease

h) hypothyroidism

i) oxytocin

j) posterior pituitary

k) progesterone

l) receptors

m) target cells

n) thymus

o) thyroid

_____ produces antidiuretic hormone

_____ stimulates uterine contractions

_____ produces thyroxine

_____ secretion that allows cellular self-control

_____ insufficient thyroxine production

_____ detect specific hormone secretion

_____ controls lipid and protein metabolism

_____ allow cells to detect stimuli

_____ regulates potassium and sodium levels

_____ blocks hormone action

_____ promotes the formation of eggs and sperm

_____ insufficient antidiuretic hormone production

_____ inflammation of the thyroid

_____ related to pregnancy and regulation of the menstrual cycle

_____ stimulates T-cell production

Fill in the missing key terms and/or definitions in the following table.

Term	Definition
	the interior region of the adrenal glands
	a hormone produced by the anterior pituitary that stimulates the adrenal cortex
agonist	
antidiuretic hormone	
	a disease caused by either insufficient insulin production or faulty insulin receptors
growth hormone	
	a chemical secretion produced inside the body that acts as a stimulus to initiate a response
islets	
ligand	
	secretions that travel via the blood or body fluids to their target cells
	an endocrine gland that is responsible for increasing blood calcium levels
pheromones	
	a hormone secreted by the kidneys in response to a decrease in blood pressure
	a hormone produced by the thymus gland that stimulates T-cell differentiation in white blood cells
thyroxine	

Label the Graphic

Identify each of the following terms in the illustration on the next page. For the hormones, write the number of the term in the appropriate space to indicate the target organ. Then answer the questions that follow.

1. anterior pituitary
2. posterior pituitary
3. nerve connection to the hypothalamus
4. adrenocorticotropic hormone
5. antidiuretic hormone
6. follicle-stimulating hormone
7. growth hormone
8. luteinizing hormone
9. melanocyte-stimulating hormone
10. oxytocin
11. prolactin
12. thyroid-stimulating hormone

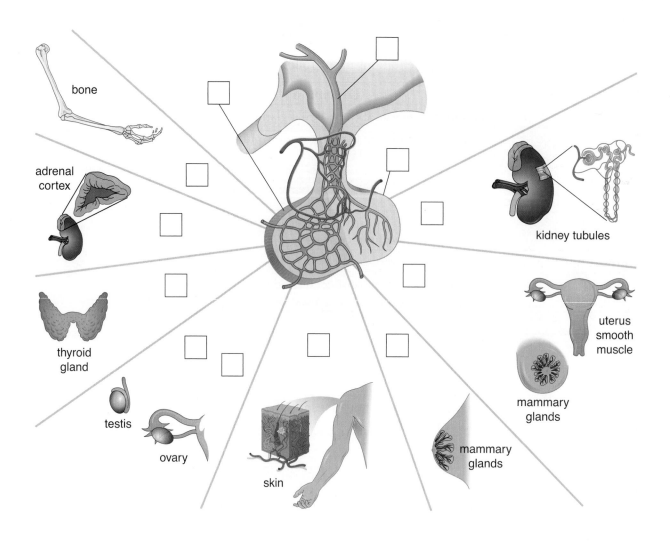

bone

adrenal cortex

kidney tubules

thyroid gland

uterus smooth muscle

testis

mammary glands

ovary

skin

mammary glands

1. Are all endocrine organs under the control of the pituitary gland? Why or why not?

2. Are all hormones in the body produced by endocrine system organs? Explain.

Color the Graphic

Color the glands in this illustration using the following color key:

adrenal – red
hypothalamus – pink
pancreas – yellow
parathyroid – black
pineal – dark green
pituitary – purple
thymus – light blue
thyroid – orange
ovaries – light green
testes – brown

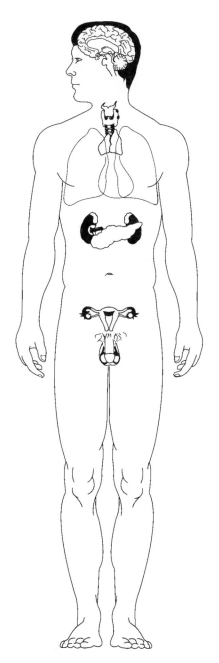

Additional Practice: The Endocrine System

Identify the location of each of the terms listed above the image. Write the name of the anatomical part on the corresponding line beneath the image.

1. Adrenal Glands

right kidney   left kidney   left suprarenal gland
inferior vena cava   right suprarenal gland

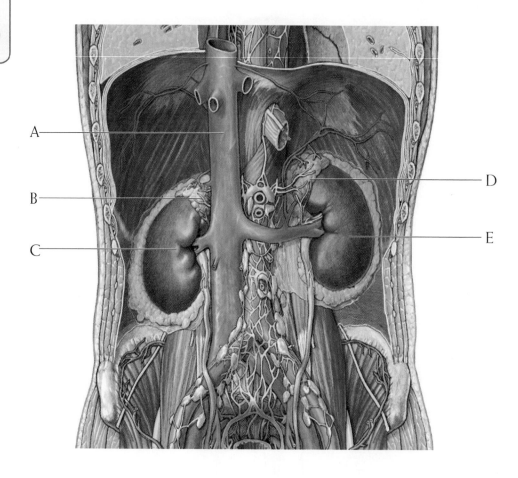

A. _____   D. _____

B. _____   E. _____

C. _____

2. Pituitary Glands

adenohypohysis/anterior pituitary   hypothalamus
neurohypophysis/posterior pituitary

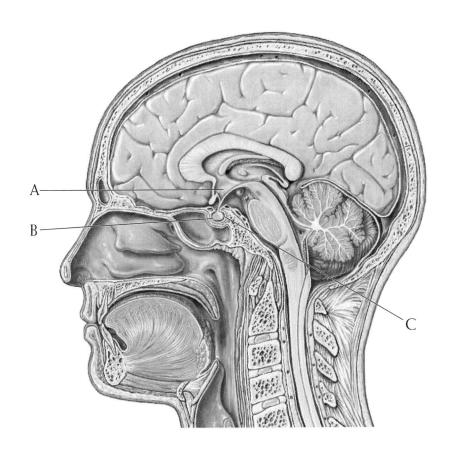

A. _____

B. _____

C. _____

You may need to reference the urinary system and reproductive system chapters (Chapters 14 and 15)to complete this exercise.

3. Ovaries

ovary   uterus   ureter

vagina   urethra   urinary bladder

pubic symphysis   uterine tube / fallopian tube

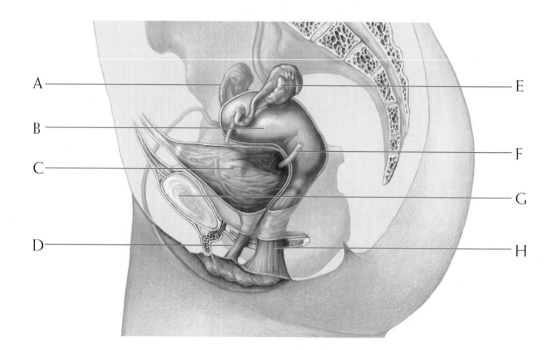

A. _____   E. _____

B. _____   F. _____

C. _____   G. _____

D. _____   H. _____

4. Pancreas

pancreas   spleen   gallbladder
bile duct   pancreatic duct

You may need to reference the digestive system chapter (Chapter 13) to complete this exercise.

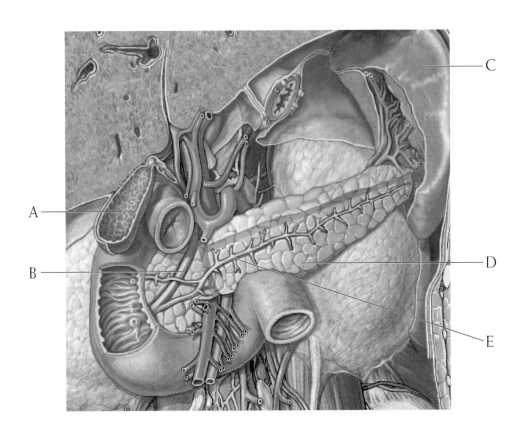

A. _____

B. _____

C. _____

D. _____

E. _____

You may need to reference the reproductive system chapter (Chapter 15)to complete this exercise.

5. Testis

seminal vesicle   prostate gland   ductus (vas) deferens
testis   pubic symphysis   urinary bladder

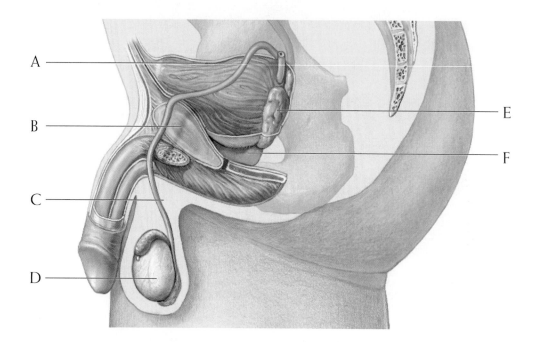

A. _____   D. _____

B. _____   E. _____

C. _____   F. _____

6. Thymus

thymus gland   trachea   superior vena cava
pericardial sac   aorta

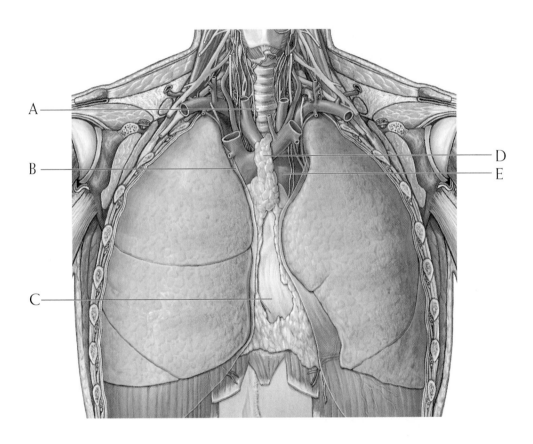

A. _____   D. _____

B. _____   E. _____

C. _____

7. Thyroid & Parathyroid

pituitary gland   hyoid bone   thyroid cartilage / larynx
thyroid gland   inferior parathyroid gland   superior parathyroid gland

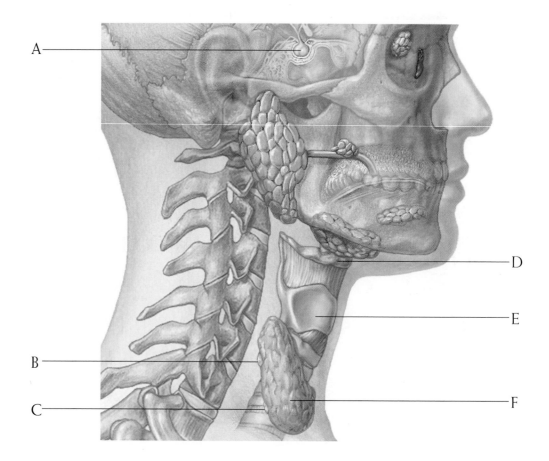

A. _____   E. _____

B. _____   F. _____

C. _____   G. _____

D. _____   H. _____

8. Glands of the Head & Neck

cricoid cartilage   thyroid cartilage   hyoid bone

manubrium   thyroid gland   trachea

You may need to reference the respiratory system chapter (Chapter 10) to complete this exercise.

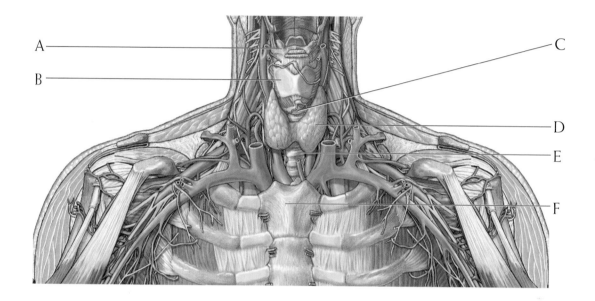

A. _____   D. _____

B. _____   E. _____

C. _____   F. _____

9. Endocrine Glands

neurohypohysis   adenohypophysis
adrenal gland   thyroid

The _____ gland is connected to the hypothalamus by the infundibulum and stores ADH and oxytocin.

The _____ gland secretes several "tropic" hormones such as TSH, ACTH, FSH, and LH.

The _____ gland secretes the hormone responsible for maintaining the body's metabolic rate.

The _____ is known as the body's "stress" gland.

Practical Application

Write brief responses to the following scenarios.

1. The pituitary gland is known as the master gland. What is the reason for this description, and do you think it is accurate? Why or why not?

2. What does the neural innervation of the hypothalamus indicate about the effect it has on the pituitary? How does this relate to the fact that the pituitary is sometimes called a "double organ"?

3. Notice the arrangement of the capillary system that leads to the pituitary gland (see Figure 7.8 in the textbook). Does this arrangement indicate anything about the control the hypothalamus has over the pituitary gland?

4. Why could a disease that affects the pituitary gland have a negative effect on the adrenal gland?

5. Explain why a particular hormone exerts its effects only on certain cells. In addition, describe how the endocrine system can be "fooled" at the receptor level.

6. Name two different roles that the cardiovascular system plays in the proper functioning of the endocrine system.

7. A hand and wrist X-ray of a child could help physicians to detect which type of hormone deficiency? How?

8. In addition to the symptoms of Addison's disease described in the text, another peculiar symptom of this disease is a tanned appearance of the skin. (In fact, President John F. Kennedy suffered from this disease, which, ironically, explains his "healthy" suntanned look.) This symptom is caused by elevated levels of adrenocorticotropic hormone (ACTH), which, at high enough levels, actually stimulates the receptors of another anterior pituitary hormone that causes the darkening of skin. Explain why ACTH levels would be elevated in someone who has this disease, and name the anterior pituitary hormone that causes the darkened skin appearance.

9. Urine tests can aid in identifying certain pathologies. A common urine analysis test can be used to detect glucose in the urine, which is an indicator of diabetes mellitus. (In persons without diabetes, normal blood glucose levels are metabolized at a rate that prevents them from being excreted.) Why would a person with diabetes mellitus be excreting glucose? What else might be detected in elevated levels in the urine?

A.D.A.M. Education

Refer to the Encyclopedia section of A.D.A.M. Interactive Anatomy. A quick search of key terms from the textbook will help you reinforce the knowledge you have gained thus far. Try entering pathological terms such as *acromegaly, Addison's disease, Cushing's disease, diabetes mellitus,* or *diabetes insipidus* in the search bar to read more about these important topics dealing with the endocrine glands and hormones.

10. Which mineral level in the body would be affected by hypoparathyroidism? Would you expect this mineral to become deficient or excessive in the body, and what other body systems would be adversely affected?

Laboratory Activity 1

Microscopic Identification of Normal Endocrine Glands

Background

Histologists and pathologists look at microscopic preparations of endocrine glands to help diagnose disease. They compare normal slides with the tissue they are examining. This helps them to determine any visible differences that may indicate an abnormality. However, before they can do this, they must practice comparing the normal samples with pictures to become familiar with the different components and cell types in the particular gland.

Materials

- Microscope with high-power capability (400X)
- Prepared slide of the pancreas
- Prepared slide of a thyroid gland
- Prepared slide of an adrenal gland

Procedure and Analysis

Place the slide of the adrenal gland under the microscope. Start with the low magnification, and move to the higher magnification to see details and individual cells. Can you find the hormone-secreting cells after comparing the slide with Figure 7.1 (below)? How do the hormone-secreting cells differ from other cells of the adrenal gland?

Figure 7.1 Adrenal Gland

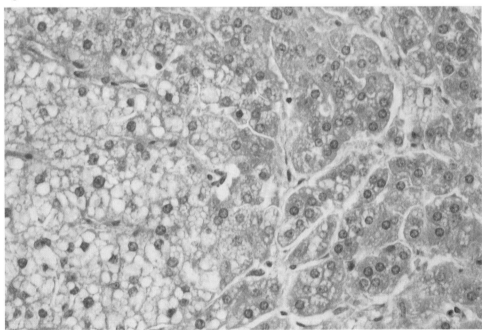

Next, look at the prepared slide of the pancreas under the microscope and compare it with Figure 7.2. Can you identify the endocrine and exocrine cells that make up this gland? What major structures are located near the hormone-secreting cells of the gland?

Figure 7.2 Pancreas

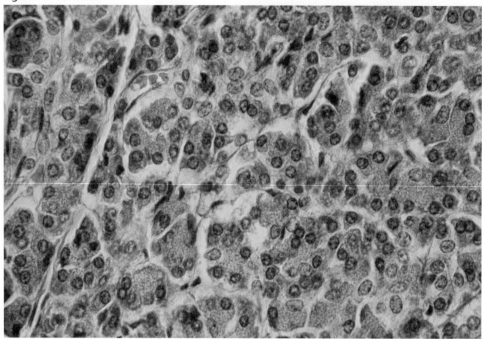

Now, look at the specimen of the thyroid gland under the microscope and compare it with Figure 7.3. How do the hormone-secreting cells of the thyroid differ from those of the pancreas? What would you expect the thyroid to look like if the patient had hyperthyroidism? What would you expect the gland to look like in a patient with hypothyroidism?

Figure 7.3 Thyroid Gland

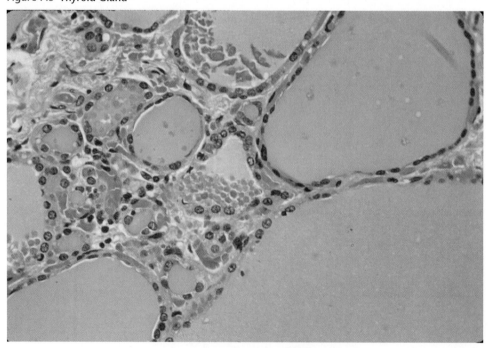

Effects of Adrenaline and Caffeine on Daphnia

Background

Adrenaline is a hormone found in almost all animals. It has essentially the same effects on human metabolism as it does on that of other animals. This laboratory activity looks at the effects of adrenaline and caffeine on the endocrine control of metabolic rate. The metabolic rate of small animals called *daphnia* will be used as a model of the human endocrine response. Daphnia are minute freshwater organisms related to crabs and shrimp. They have a round body enclosed in a transparent shell. Animal models such as daphnia are useful and important for obtaining preliminary laboratory data on humans.

Materials

- Daphnia, kept in a container of clean fresh water
- Large container of clean water (for used daphnia)
- Droppers for collecting and transporting the daphnia
- Microscope
- Droppers for collecting samples of epinephrine, caffeine, and coffee or tea
- Three clean microscope slides per observation
- Over-the-counter epinephrine preparation (asthma pills) soaked in 100 mL of a 50% ethyl alchohol/50% water mixture
- One 100-mg caffeine pill soaked in 100 mL of a 50% ethyl alchohol/50% water mixture
- Half-strength coffee or tea
- Surgical gloves

Precautions It is recommended that you wear surgical gloves when handling the epinephrine and caffeine solutions. All of the solutions can be stored in labeled bottles in the refrigerator for two to three weeks. Excess solution should be flushed down a drain.

Note Brine shrimp or other small invertebrates can be used in place of daphnia. Brine shrimp must be kept in the salt solution used to raise them. Remember not to use fresh water on the slides used to observe brine shrimp.

Procedure

Use a dropper to place some daphnia on the microscope slide. Observe their normal behavior. Make sure you keep adding water to the slide to keep them from drying out and dying. Keep track of the speed at which they move around and how fast they move their feet. Add one drop of the epinephrine solution to the daphnia. Note what happens to their movement. Place the daphnia in the used daphnia container, and place another set of daphnia on a new clean slide. Repeat the steps using the caffeine pills. Record your observations. Again, recycle the daphnia, and collect another batch to record the effects of a drop of coffee or tea.

Analysis

Write a one- to two-page analysis of your findings. Answer the following questions in your report:

1. What effects does the epinephrine have on the daphnia?
2. How does the effect of the caffeine pill compare with adrenaline?
3. How does the effect of tea or coffee differ from that of epinephrine and caffeine?
4. What else is present in coffee or tea that might affect the metabolic rate of animals?

Quiz

1. True or False: All glands of the endocrine system function exclusively for hormone production.

2. The number of endocrine glands (consider a "paired" gland as one gland) that make up the endocrine system is:
   a) twelve
   b) eight
   c) six
   d) nine

3. Endocrine glands produce secretions:
   a) that travel directly to the body area they affect
   b) used only by other endocrine glands
   c) in response to signals from the environment or from other cells
   d) All of the above

4. Hormones produced by endocrine glands reach their target cells because:
   a) target cells have specialized receptors that detect specific hormones
   b) specialized capillary systems direct specific hormones to specific locations
   c) hormones can be sent directly through ducts connecting endocrine organs to their target cells
   d) All of the above

5. Which of the following statements is true?
   a) When a hormone binds to a receptor, it causes biochemical changes to the target cell.
   b) Hormones are stimuli that, when detected by receptors, elicit a response from an effector.
   c) Target cells possess receptors and act as effectors.
   d) All of the above

6. Hormone receptors are categorized as internal when they:
   a) interact with a specific portion of the carrier proteins DNA when stimulated
   b) rely on carrier proteins to receive their specific hormones
   c) are located on the cell membrane
   d) All of the above

7. Endocrine system secretions described as *autocrine*:
   a) regulate other endocrine organs
   b) leave the body and signal cells of other organisms
   c) do not travel through the blood to reach their target cells
   d) travel via body fluids to their receptor cells

8. The negative feedback system that many endocrine glands utilize:
   a) is a type of self-regulation
   b) ensures that hormone production will continue until "shut-off" by another body system
   c) relies on exocrine-gland interaction
   d) All of the above

9. Chemicals that can act as hormones:
   a) may be medically advantageous
   b) may be considered environmental risk factors
   c) are sometimes referred to as hormone mimics
   d) All of the above

10. Insufficient levels of cholesterol in the body might interfere with the production of:
    a) any peptide hormone
    b) steroids
    c) all lipid hormones
    d) All of the above

11. Which of the following statements is true?
    a) Lipid hormones and peptide hormones play equal roles in long-term body effects.
    b) Most lipid hormones usually have a short-term influence on the body.
    c) Most lipid hormones have long-term effects on the body.
    d) Protein hormones cannot be removed from the body.

12. The pituitary gland is:
    a) self-regulated
    b) under control of the hypothalamus
    c) stimulated by hormones of other endocrine glands
    d) All of the above

13. The posterior pituitary gland produces hormones:
    a) that influence water loss
    b) that influence many other endocrine organs
    c) involved in self-regulation
    d) All of the above

14. Leutinizing hormone stimulates:
    a) gamete production in both sexes
    b) sperm production only
    c) egg production only
    d) production of estrogen and testosterone

15. Which of the following would most likely occur from abnormal growth hormone production?
    a) no serious effects, due to compensation by other endocrine glands
    b) dwarfism or gigantism
    c) effects on reproductive capabilities only
    d) atrophy of the pituitary gland

16. Light therapy can be used to treat symptoms that result from lack of:
    a) prolactin
    b) ACTH
    c) melatonin
    d) ADH

17. Glucocorticoids and minerocorticoids are produced by the:
    a) kidneys
    b) anterior pituitary
    c) adrenal medulla
    d) adrenal cortex

18. The production of epinephrine and norepinephrine:
    a) occurs in the adrenal medulla
    b) is initiated in response to stress, heavy physical exertion, or low blood glucose
    c) initiates release of glucose and fat into the blood
    d) All of the above

19. Low levels of thyroxine production would most likely result in:
    a) weight gain
    b) elevated body temperatures
    c) increased heart rate
    d) All of the above

20. Blood calcium levels are controlled by:
    a) the thyroid gland
    b) the parathyroid glands
    c) calcitonin
    d) All of the above

21. Damage to the beta cells of the pancreas would most likely result in:
    a) decreased insulin production
    b) decreased glucagon production
    c) decreased blood glucose levels
    d) All of the above

22. Abnormal T-cell production would indicate an abnormality in which endocrine organ?
    a) the thyroid
    b) the parathyroids
    c) the thymus
    d) All of the above

23. Which of the following diseases can be thought of as opposites?
    a) diabetes mellitus and diabetes insipidus
    b) Cushing's disease and Addison's disease
    c) Grave's disease and hyperthyroidism
    d) hypoactive growth-hormone production and dwarfism

24. The sex hormones:
    a) are elevated during puberty
    b) exert influence during fetal development
    c) are decreased in older age
    d) All of the above

25. Aging of the digestive system affects endocrine function because:
    a) digestion requires increased energy
    b) elevated hormones are excreted from the body
    c) absorption of certain nutrients necessary for hormone production is
       decreased
    d) neural innervation necessary for hormone activity is lost

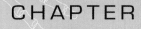

CHAPTER

8 FUNCTION OF THE NERVOUS SYSTEM

Introduction

The nervous system plays a vital role in the maintenance of homeostasis in the body. The organs of the nervous system contain specialized receptors that respond to a variety of internal and external stimuli such as touch, temperature, light, chemicals, and pain. The nervous system also interprets these stimuli, allowing the body to quickly adapt and react to all types of internal and external environmental changes. The following exercises and lab activities will require you to apply what you have learned about nervous system function. For assistance, refer to Chapter 8 of *Applied Anatomy & Physiology, A Case Study Approach*. You may also access A.D.A.M. Interactive Anatomy for additional information to expand your understanding of the concepts presented in the textbook.

Completion

Complete the following sentences by filling in each blank with a key term from the text.

1. _____ are categorized by their cell anatomy, while _____ are classified by the way in which they assist nerve cells.

2. Four common features of all neurons are: the _____ _____ _____, _____, _____, and _____.

3. _____ can only receive information from other cells, while _____ transmit information but can also receive information through a(n) _____ _____.

4. Most _____ neurons produce only one type of neurotransmitter, but _____ neurons can contain a variety of neurotransmitter receptors.

5. Neurons have three primary shapes: _____, _____, and _____.

6. Neuroglia called astrocytes help form a protective feature called the _____-_____ _____, while ependymal cell neuroglia produce _____ _____.

7. The _____ _____ charge inside the cell is -70 millivolts (mV), but when a(n) _____ _____ occurs, the increased flow of sodium into the cell causes the cell to reach a stage called _____.

8. _____ neurotransmitters cause the sodium channels to open, initiating an action potential, while _____ neurotransmitters make it more difficult for the neuron to achieve an action potential.

9. In a reflex arc, the _____ receives stimuli and the _____ responds to it.

10. Nerve cell diseases can be categorized into five major groups: infectious, degenerative, _____, _____, and _____.

Matching

Match each of the following terms with the corresponding description by writing the letter of the term on the blank next to the correct description.

a) amyotropical lateral sclerosis (ALS)

b) catecholamine

c) cytokines

d) gamma amniobutiric acid (GABA)

e) hyperpolarization

f) internal stimuli

g) interneurons

h) lipofuscin

i) neurotrophic

j) propagate

k) Schwann cells

l) soma

m) synaptic cleft

n) threshold

o) terminus

_____ produce myelin

_____ cell secretions used to communicate information

_____ to travel across

_____ point of sodium-channel opening

_____ gap at the nerve terminus

_____ inhibitory amino acid neurotransmitter

_____ indicates nerve cell pathology

_____ nerve cell body

_____ bipolar neuron dendrites

_____ genetic degenerative disorder

_____ maintain cell health and activity

_____ more negative potential than resting potential

_____ excitatory neurotransmitter

_____ capable of invading neurons

_____ site of neurotransmitter release

Complete the Terms Table

Fill in the missing key terms and/or definitions in the following table.

Term	Definition
	environmental factors that influence metabolic changes in a cell or physiological changes in tissues and organs
neural tube	
	the region of the nerve cell body from which the axon extends
	neuron cell extensions that receive stimuli
	neuroglial cells that help maintain the chemical environment of neurons and may help in nerve cell repair
nodes of Ranvier	
	the action-potential stage following repolarization during which a normal stimulation will not cause another action potential
tetany	
	a catecholamine neurotransmitter that can be inhibitory as well as excitatory
innervate	
reverberating pathway	
	involuntary responses to a stimulus
	inflammation of membranes surrounding the brain
	a neurotrophic disease caused by infectious prions that can be contracted through exposure to the blood and meat of infected animals
tonic control	

Label the Graphic

Identify each of the following terms in the illustration on the next page. Write the number of the neuron part in the box indicating its location. Some terms will be used more than once. When you are finished, answer the questions that follow.

1. axon
2. cell body
3. axon hillock
4. dendrite

5. myelin sheath
6. receptor cell
7. terminus

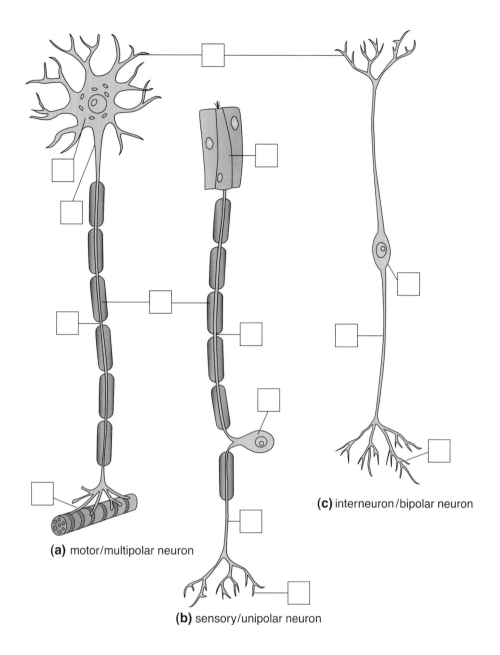

(a) motor/multipolar neuron

(b) sensory/unipolar neuron

(c) interneuron/bipolar neuron

1. How would you describe the shape of each of the illustrated neuron types?

2. In what order would the neuron types be arranged in a reflex arc?

Color the Graphic

Color the illustration below using the following color key. Then answer the question that follows.

Neuroglial cells
    astrocytes – red
    ependymal cells – pink
    microglial cells – yellow
    oligodendrites – green

Neuron anatomy
    axons – light blue
    dendrites – brown
    myelin sheath – dark blue
    soma – orange

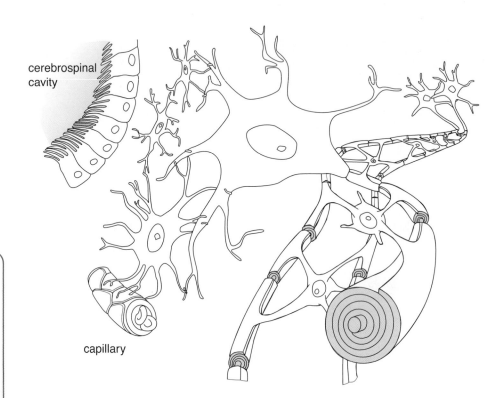

cerebrospinal cavity

capillary

A.D.A.M. Education

To view an animated presentation of nerve conduction, click on the Clinical Animations tab within A.D.A.M. Interactive Anatomy. Refine your search by choosing *Neurology* from the Body System tab, clicking the search button, and then choosing the *Nerve conduction — general overview* animation.

Does this illustration represent nervous tissue in the central nervous system or in the peripheral nervous system? Give the evidence for your answer.

Practical Application

Write brief responses to the following scenarios.

1. Describe a typical reflex arc in terms of the most likely shape of the neuron at each portion of the arc.

2. How can the same neurotransmitter be described as being both excitatory and inhibitory?

3. Can a chemical synapse cause an action potential to occur in both directions of a neural pathway?

4. Describe the action potential terms *depolarize, hyperpolarize,* and *repolarize* relative to resting potential. For each term, indicate what has occurred to cause the change in membrane potential measurement.

5. Would a drug described as being antagonistic to a neurotransmitter increase or decrease the normal neurotransmitter response? What might be the mechanism of such a drug if it were to exert its effects on the post-synaptic side of the synaptic cleft?

6. What type of pathology might be indicated by the presence of an extremely high number of microglial cells in the nervous system?

7. Compare and contrast Schwann cells and oligodendritic cells.

8. Epilepsy is characterized by uncontrolled excitatory neuronal activity. Could this disease be caused by a lack of glutamate or GABA?

9. The disease amyotrophic lateral sclerosis (ALS) is characterized by scar tissue that forms sclerotic (hardened) areas in the areas of the spinal cord that control the diaphragm and intercostal muscles, resulting in a progressive loss of innervation to these muscles. Explain why this disease can be fatal.

10. Neurons are more susceptible to the negative consequences of aging than are many other types of cells in the body. Briefly discuss two characteristics of neuron cells that contribute to this vulnerability.

Laboratory Activity 1

Pupil Reflex

Background

One way to monitor the health of nerves is to observe reflex responses. The body possesses a variety of reflexes that respond to various stimuli. Physicians can track specific nerves by investigating reflexes unique to that nerve. The pupil reflex response is used to indicate the health of a particular nerve in the brain. This nerve can be an indirect indicator of brain damage due to disease or injury. Reflexes are important indicators of aging and pathology. The speed at which a reflex occurs differs from person to person, and also depends upon his or her experiences and level of attentiveness at the time.

Materials

- Small flashlight with a dim bulb
- Small ruler
- Ability to darken the room, or use of a dark location
- Stopwatch or clock with a second hand

Procedure

1. Have your lab partner sit in a chair. Make sure you can easily see his or her eyes.
2. Dim the lights in the room, and wait for 3 minutes.
3. Place the ruler near the subject's left eye, and measure the diameter of the pupil. Record the measurement.
4. With the bulb off, place the flashlight 12 inches from the subject's left eye. Aim it straight at the center of the eye.
5. Set the stopwatch to zero, and simultaneously start the stopwatch and turn on the flashlight.
6. Measure and record the time it takes for the pupil to close tightly.
7. Again, measure and record the diameter of the pupil.
8. Repeat steps 1 through 7 for the right eye.
9. To obtain the most accurate data, repeat the experiment three times for each eye.
10. Calculate the following information for each pupil:
    a. average time it takes the pupil to respond to light
    b. average change in pupil diameter
11. Place the data on a chart with the data from other subjects. See Table 8.1 for an example.

Table 8.1

Pupil Reflex						
Subject Name:						
	Left Eye			**Right Eye**		
	Starting diameter of pupil	Time for pupil to close	Ending diameter of pupil	Starting diameter of pupil	Time for pupil to close	Ending diameter of pupil
Trial 1						
Trial 2						
Trial 3						
Subject Name:						
	Left Eye			**Right Eye**		
	Starting diameter of pupil	Time for pupil to close	Ending diameter of pupil	Starting diameter of pupil	Time for pupil to close	Ending diameter of pupil
Trial 1						
Trial 2						
Trial 3						
Subject Name:						
	Left Eye			**Right Eye**		
	Starting diameter of pupil	Time for pupil to close	Ending diameter of pupil	Starting diameter of pupil	Time for pupil to close	Ending diameter of pupil
Trial 1						
Trial 2						
Trial 3						

Analysis

Analyze the information you recorded and compare it with the data recorded by your classmates. Write a one- to two-paragraph analysis that answers the following questions:

1. Are there any differences in reflex time between the right and left eyes of the subjects?
2. What are some possible reasons for differences in response time in the pupils of one individual?
3. Are there any differences between individuals in the average time it takes for the pupils to respond to light?
4. Are there any differences between individuals in the average change in diameter of the pupils?
5. What are some possible reasons for any differences in response between the pupils of different individuals?

Knee-Jerk Reflex

Background

As noted in Laboratory Activity 1, one way to monitor the health of nerves is to observe reflex responses. The knee-jerk reflex is a general indicator of nervous system function. It involves two sets of long nerve cells that communicate information up and down the length of the upper leg and into the lower lumbar region. Reflexes are important indicators of aging and pathology. The speed at which a reflex occurs differs from person to person, and also depends upon his or her experiences and level of attentiveness at the time.

Materials

- Patella reflex hammer (optional)
- Stopwatch or clock with a second hand
- Stable table (to sit on)

Procedure

1. Have your lab partner sit on a table with his or her left leg crossed over the right leg. The crossed leg should be able to swing freely.
2. Set the stopwatch to zero.
3. Start the stopwatch as you quickly, but gently, hit the crossed leg just below the knee with a patella reflex hammer or the side of your hand.
4. Measure and record the time it takes for the subject's leg to kick out and return to the resting position.
5. Repeat the procedure at least three times.
6. Repeat steps 1 through 5 for the right leg.
7. Record the data in a chart like the one in Table 8.2, and compare your data with the data recorded by your classmates.

Table 8.2

Subject Name:		
	Left Leg	**Right Leg**
	Time Recorded	Time Recorded
Trial 1		
Trial 2		
Trial 3		

Analysis

Analyze the information you recorded, and compare it with the data recorded by your classmates. Write a one- to two-paragraph analysis that answers the following questions:

1. Are there any differences in reflexes between the right and left legs of the subjects?
2. What are some possible reasons for any differences in response between the left and right knee-jerk reflexes of one individual?
3. Are there any differences in reflexes between the subjects?
4. What are some possible reasons for differences in reflex time between individuals?

Laboratory Activity 3

Catch Reflex

Background

Recall that one way to monitor the health of nerves is to observe reflex responses. The body possesses a variety of reflexes that respond to various stimuli. Physicians can track specific nerves by investigating reflexes unique to that nerve. Observation of the "catch" reflex involves measuring the time it takes a person to communicate information from the eye, as it detects a dropped object, to the arm and hand, to make a movement to catch the object. Reflexes are important indicators of aging and pathology. The speed at which a reflex occurs differs from person to person, and also depends upon his or her experiences and level of attentiveness at the time.

Materials

- 12-inch ruler
- Meter stick

Procedure

1. Have your lab partner stand upright, at least 2 feet away from any chairs or tables.
2. Stand facing your lab partner.
3. Hold a 12-inch ruler by the upper end, and let it hang down in front of the subject. You should be holding the ruler by the highest number , and the lowest number should be down toward the floor.
4. Have your partner put his or her left hand near the bottom of the ruler. He or she should be ready to grab the ruler, but should not be touching the ruler at this point.
5. Tell the subject that you will drop the ruler sometime within the next 5 seconds, and that he or she should catch it when it drops.
6. Release the ruler.
7. Record the inch or centimeter marking at which the subject caught the ruler. If the subject could not catch the ruler in time, try using a meter stick instead.
8. Repeat this test at least three times.
9. Convert the ruler markings you recorded into reaction times using the chart in Table 8.4. Record the reaction times.
10. Repeat steps 3 through 9 for the subject's right hand.
11. Record the data in a chart with the data from your classmates' experiments (see Table 8.3).

Table 8.3

Subject Name:		
	Left Hand	Right Hand
	Time Recorded	Time Recorded
Trial 1		
Trial 2		
Trial 3		

Table 8.4

Distance Marking		Time
Inches (in)	Centimeters (cm)	Seconds (sec)
2	5.1	0.10
4	10.2	0.14
6	15.3	0.17
8	20.4	0.20
10	25.5	0.23
12	30.0	0.25
17	42.5	0.30
24	60.0	0.35
31	77.5	0.40

Analysis

Analyze the information you recorded and compare it with the data recorded by your classmates. Write a one- to two-paragraph analysis that answers the following questions:

1. Are there any differences between the left and right arm catch reflexes of the subjects?
2. What are some possible reasons for any differences in response between the left and right arm catch reflexes of one individual?
3. Are there any differences in reflexes between the subjects?
4. What are some possible reasons for any differences in response between the left and right arm catch reflexes of different individuals?

1. True or False: Neuroglial cells are the only cells of the nervous system thought to function in nerve cell repair.

2. Sunlight is an example of:
   a) an affector
   b) an external stimulus
   c) a receptor
   d) All of the above

3. Which of the following statements best describes neurons and neuroglia?
   a) They function independently of one another.
   b) They are distributed in equal numbers throughout the nervous system.
   c) They are derived from neural stem cells.
   d) All of the above

4. The synaptic cleft could be located at:
   a) a dendrite of a presynaptic neuron
   b) the terminus of a postsynaptic neuron
   c) the terminus of a presynaptic neuron
   d) All of the above

5. Motor neurons are:
   a) unipolar
   b) multipolar
   c) bipolar
   d) All of the above

6. Which of the following neuroglial types could be described as the "gatekeeper" between the vascular and nervous systems?
   a) Schwann cells
   b) satellite cells
   c) astrocytes
   d) ependymal cells

7. Which of the following best describes a cell at resting potential?
   a) The inside of the cell is more positively charged than is the surrounding environment.
   b) The inside of the cell is more negatively charged than is its surrounding environment.
   c) The cell has a charge equivalent to its external environment.
   d) The cell is not in an excitable condition.

8. At threshold, the cytoplasm's charge is:
   a) more negative than at resting potential
   b) becoming more negative due to gaining potassium
   c) changing due to loss of sodium
   d) more positive than at resting potential

9. Depolarization:
   a) is characterized by the cell's interior being more positive than its exterior
   b) precedes repolarization
   c) accompanies the release of the neurotransmitter into the synaptic cleft
   d) All of the above

10. Action potential propagation is accelerated by:
    a) an influx of calcium
    b) the presence of myelin sheaths along the axon
    c) hyperpolarization
    d) All of the above

11. Which of the following best describes neurotransmitters?
    a) They are released by the presynaptic neuron.
    b) They transfer the action potential from a sensory neuron to a motor neuron.
    c) They can be excitatory or inhibitory.
    d) All of the above

12. Neurotransmitters that are similar to the hormones made by the adrenal medulla are classified as:
    a) monoamines
    b) catecholamines
    c) amino-acid derivatives
    d) cholinergic

13. A diet containing no fat would decrease the production of which of the following neurotransmitters?
    a) serotonin
    b) dopamine
    c) acetylcholine
    d) All of the above

14. Which of the following best describes a reverberating neural pathway?
    a) It is a type of axon self-stimulation.
    b) It is inhibitory.
    c) It results from an axosomatic synapse.
    d) All of the above

15. Reflexes:
    a) are involuntary neural responses
    b) are controlled by a neural pathway called a reflex arc
    c) transmit stimuli from the environment through an afferent neuron
    d) All of the above

16. Interneurons of a reflex arc are responsible for:
    a) detecting the initial stimulus
    b) consciously modifying certain reflexes
    c) directly innervating a muscle or gland
    d) All of the above

17. Flaccid paralysis might result from:
    a) excessive production of excitatory neurotransmitter
    b) excessive production of catecholamine
    c) loss of acetylcholine reuptake
    d) inability of acetylcholine to bind to postsynaptic receptors

18. Which of the following would most likely result from the production of bacterial endotoxin?
    a) inflammation
    b) paralysis
    c) demyelination
    d) All of the above

19. Which of the following diseases is acquired before birth?
    a) Krabbe's disease
    b) Lou Gehrig's disease (ALS)
    c) Hirschsprung's disease
    d) All of the above

20. Creutzfeldt-Jakob disease is:
    a) caused by prions
    b) similar to mad cow disease
    c) transmissible through contact with certain body tissues
    d) All of the above

21. Herpes can be categorized as a disease that is:
    a) neurotrophic
    b) infectious
    c) degenerative
    d) All of the above

22. Certain types of infectious diseases can also be classified as:
    a) toxicological
    b) traumatic
    c) developmental
    d) All of the above

23. Traumatic injury resulting in neuron loss can be repaired by:
    a) damaged neurons undergoing mitosis
    b) associated neuroglial cells
    c) macrophages
    d) All of the above

24. Which of the following statements is true?
    a) Neuron cells replicate throughout an individual's life.
    b) Neuron cells have a relatively low metabolic rate.
    c) The number of neurons an individual has does not change throughout his or her life span.
    d) When a neuron dies it cannot be replaced.

25. Which of the following is a result of nerve cell aging?
    a) loss of tonic control
    b) decreased blood flow
    c) oxidation by metabolic waste products
    d) decreased nutrient absorption

CHAPTER

9 STRUCTURE OF THE NERVOUS SYSTEM

Introduction

The nervous system is divided into two major components: the central nervous system and the peripheral nervous system. The central nervous system consists of the brain and spinal cord. The peripheral nervous system consists of sensory nerves (which carry information from receptors towards the brain for interpretation) and motor nerves (which convey information from control centers in the brain to the tissues). Special senses such as smell, taste, vision, hearing, and balance utilize nerve receptors specifically modified to transmit information related to that sense. The following exercises and lab activities will require you to apply what you have learned about the structure of the nervous system and special sense organs. If you need assistance, refer to Chapter 9 of *Applied Anatomy & Physiology: A Case Study Approach*. Additionally, you can access A.D.A.M. Interactive Anatomy for information that will expand your understanding of the concepts presented in the textbook.

Completion

Complete the following sentences by filling in each blank with a key term from the text.

1. Sensory information usually travels from the _____ nervous system to the _____ nervous system.

2. The nerves that carry information from sensory receptors to the brain and spinal cord are called _____, while those that convey information from the central nervous system to muscles or glands are called _____.

3. The three layers of the meninges in order from deep to superficial are the _____ _____, the _____, and the _____ _____.

4. Brain and spinal cord tissue composed primarily of neurons is referred to as _____ _____ due to the darker pigmentation of its fat component, while the tissue of the central nervous system, which is composed primarily of axons and myelin, is called _____ _____.

5. The three developmental divisions of the brain are called the _____, _____, and _____.

6. The four lobes of the cerebral hemispheres are the _____, _____, _____, and _____.

7. The hindbrain consists of three distinct portions called the _____, _____ _____, and _____.

8. The two divisions of the peripheral nervous system are the _____ and _____ branches.

9. Motor nerves stem from the _____ _____ of the spinal cord, while sensory nerves stem from the _____ _____.

10. Cranial and spinal nerves give rise to the_____ division of the _____ nervous system, but the _____ division arises from the thoracic and lumbar regions.

Matching

Match each of the following terms with the corresponding description by writing the letter of the term on the blank next to the correct description.

a) abducens

b) audition

c) central sulcus

d) choroid plexus

e) epineurium

f) glioma

g) gustation

h) hypoglossal

i) insula

j) meninges

k) papillae

l) plasticity

m) rhodopsin

n) ventricles

o) vestibule

_____ neuroglial tumor

_____ site of taste buds

_____ memory processing

_____ brain cavities

_____ detects body position

_____ brain and spinal cord membrane

_____ result of neuron experience

_____ light-sensitive chemical

_____ outer nerve covering

_____ provides signals for eye movement

_____ hearing

_____ makes cerebrospinal fluid

_____ sense of taste

_____ separates frontal and parietal lobes

_____ controls tongue movement

Complete the Terms Table

Fill in the missing key terms and/or definitions in the following table.

Term	Definition
redundancy	
	a nervous system disorder that causes slow, involuntary movements of the hands and feet
	a tumor that develops from nervous system cells
arteriovenous malformation	
	a disorder of blood vessels in the brain
semicircular canals	
	a depression in the retina that contains only cones
	the clear covering at the front surface of the eye that permits light to enter
olfactory bulb	
	a cranial nerve that is sensory for transmitting cardiovascular reflexes and has motor control of the heart and digestion
extrapyramidal tract	
	a collection of nuclei at the base of the cerebrum that is associated with emotions
ventricles	
	the cerebral lobe that interprets vision and assists with eye function
	a band of white matter that connects the left and right hemispheres of the cerebrum

Label the Graphic

Identify each of the following cranial nerves in the illustration below. Write the number of the nerve in the box indicating its location. Then answer the questions that follow.

1. abducens
2. accessory
3. facial
4. glossopharyngeal

5. hypoglossal
6. oculomotor
7. olfactory
8. optic

9. trigeminal
10. trochlear
11. vagus
12. vestibular

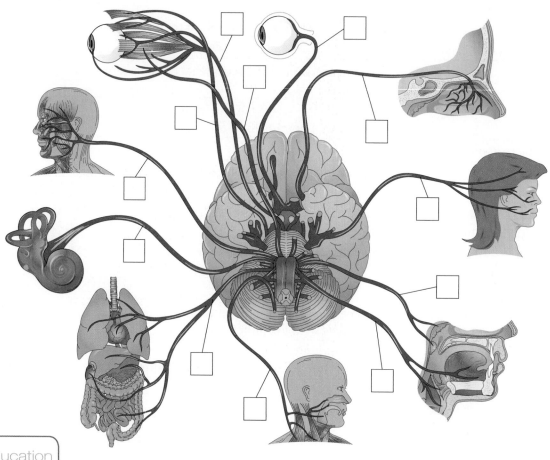

1. Which of the cranial nerves have sensory function?

2. Which have motor function?

Color the Graphic

Color the illustration using the following key. Then answer the questions that follow.

brain stem – orange
central sulcus – black
cerebellum – pink

frontal lobe – blue
lateral fissure – brown
occipital lobe – yellow

parietal lobe – green
temporal lobe – red

❋ A.D.A.M. Education

Refer to A.D.A.M. Interactive Anatomy for three-dimensional models of the brain, ear, and eye. Click on the 3D Anatomy tab within AIA and choose the desired 3D model. You will then be able to turn the models to observe them from all views.

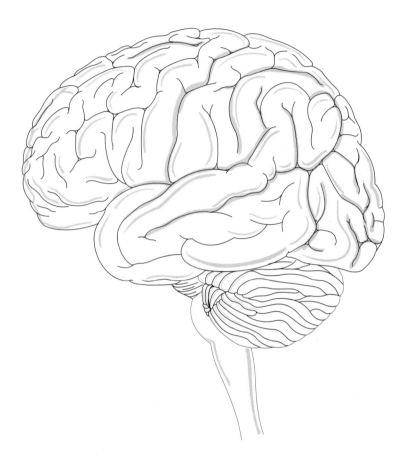

❋ A.D.A.M. Education

For additional information on common conditions associated with the nervous system, access A.D.A.M. Interactive Anatomy and then click the Clinical Illustrations tab. Narrow your search by choosing *Nervous* from the Body System menu. A quick search will lead you to a variety of images to explore, including the brain, eye anatomy, ear anatomy, meninges, autonomic nerves, the limbic system, vision, ear tube insertion, nerve damage, stroke, and LASIK eye surgery.

1. The forebrain is made up of which parts of the brain?

2. Describe the position of the cerebellum and medulla oblongata in relation to the pons.

3. Which developmental portion of the brain is made up of the cerebellum, pons, and medulla oblongata?

4. Which developmental portion of the brain is located between the forebrain and hindbrain?

For additional assistance on the labeling exercises, open A.D.A.M. Interactive Anatomy and click the Atlas Anatomy tab. Next, refine your search by selecting *Nervous* from the Body System menu and *Illustration* from the Image Type menu. Refine your search by choosing the appropriate Body Region from the drop down menu. To find examples of organs that contribute to more than one body system (i.e. the tongue or ear) enter the desired name in the search bar at the top of the screen and match the options with the images presented here.

Additional Practice: The Nervous System

Identify the location of each of the terms listed above the image. Write the name of the anatomical part on the corresponding line beneath the image.

1. Brain (Lat)

parietal lobe   occipital lobe   cerebellum
medulla oblongata   spinal cord   pons
temporal lobe   frontal lobe

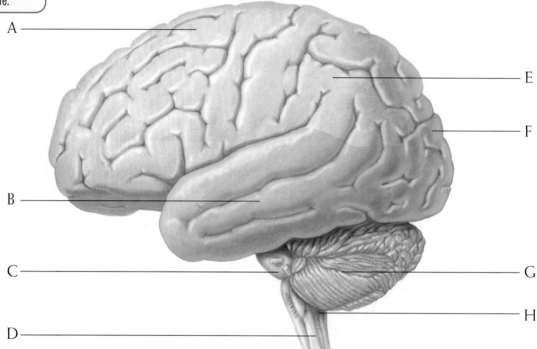

A. _____   E. _____

B. _____   F. _____

C. _____   G. _____

D. _____   H. _____

2. Base of Brain (Inf) and Cranial Nerves

olfactory nerve   optic nerve   medulla oblongata
pituitary gland   pons   temporal lobe
spinal cord   cerebellum   frontal lobe
occipital lobe   trigeminal nerve

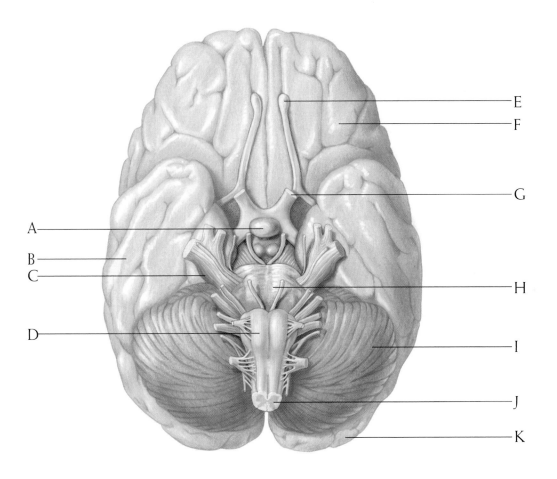

A. _____   G. _____

B. _____   H. _____

C. _____   I. _____

D. _____   J. _____

E. _____   K. _____

F. _____

A.D.A.M. Education

3. Spinal Cord Vessels & Meninges

ventral nerve root   dorsal nerve root
spinal nerve   dorsal root ganglion

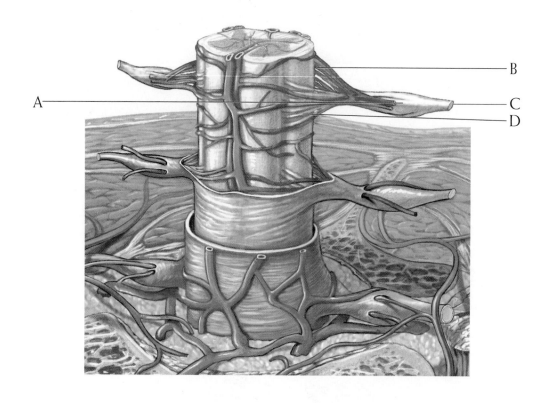

A. _____   C. _____

B. _____   D. _____

4. Nerves of Upper Limb (Ant)

ulnar nerve
musculocutaneous nerve

median nerve
axillary nerve

radial nerve

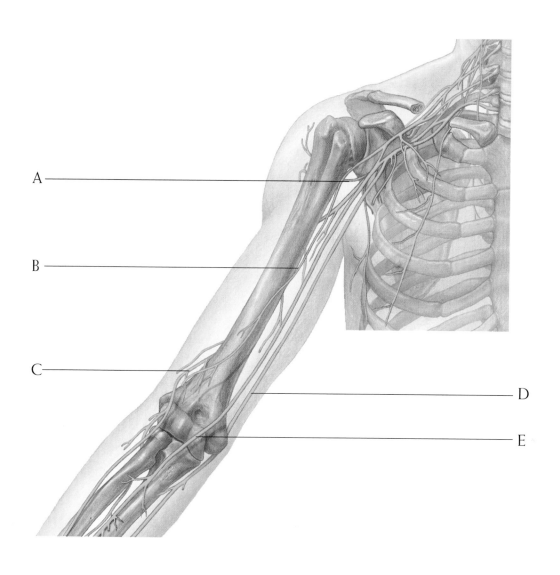

A. _____

B. _____

C. _____

D. _____

E. _____

5. Sacral Plexus

psoas major muscle   femoral nerve   sciatic nerve
sacral plexus   iliacus muscle

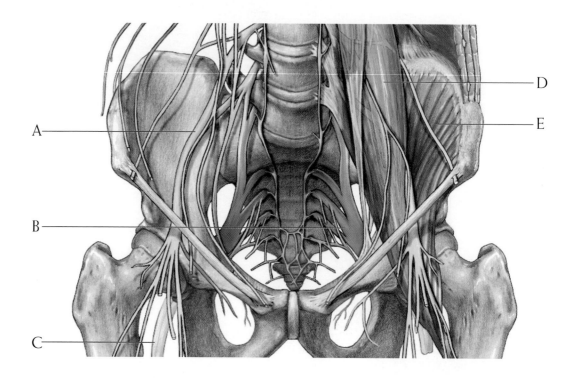

A. _____   D. _____

B. _____   E. _____

C. _____

6. Tongue and Tastes

epiglottis   bitter   sour
lingual tonsil   salty   sweet

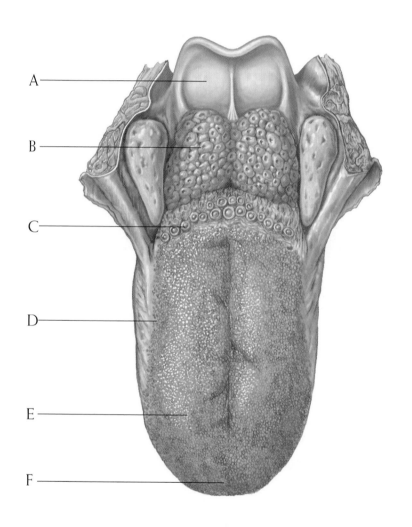

A. _____   D. _____
B. _____   E. _____
C. _____   F. _____

You may need to reference the skeletal system chapter (Chapter 5) to complete this exercise.

7. Olfactory Nerve

frontal sinus   olfactory nerve filaments   olfactory nerve
ethmoid bone   external nares / nostril   sphenoidal sinus
hard palate

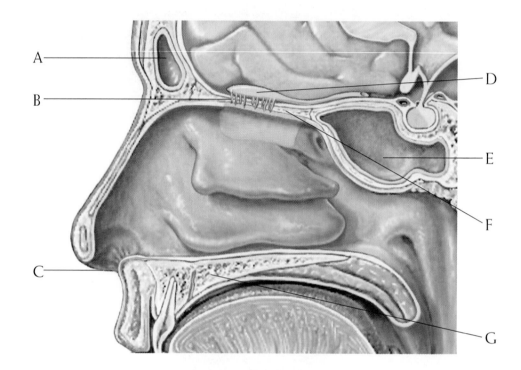

A. _____   E. _____

B. _____   F. _____

C. _____   G. _____

D. _____

8. External Eye

conjunctiva   iris   pupil

sclera   maxilla   zygomatic bone

frontal bone   lacrimal bone

You may need to reference the skeletal system chapter (Chapter 5) to complete this exercise.

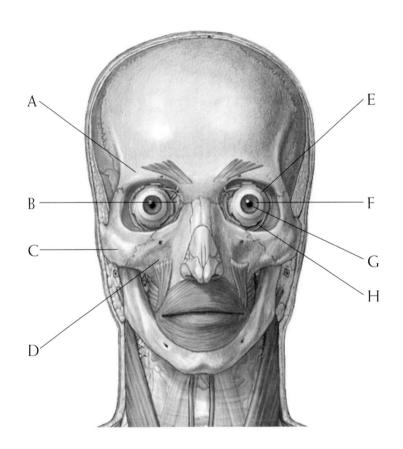

A. _____   E. _____

B. _____   F. _____

C. _____   G. _____

D. _____   H. _____

🌸A.D.A.M. Education

9. Eye Muscles

superior rectus
optic nerve
lateral rectus

superior oblique
inferior rectus

medial rectus
inferior oblique

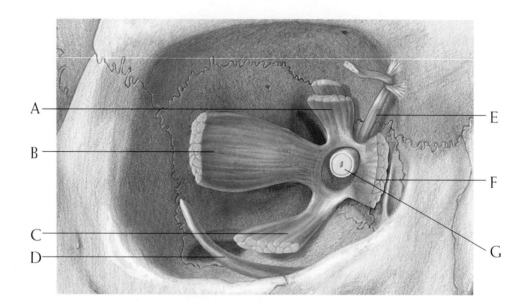

A. _____   E. _____

B. _____   F. _____

C. _____   G. _____

D. _____

10. Eye Muscles (Lat)

superior rectus   superior oblique   lateral rectus
inferior oblique   inferior rectus   medial rectus
optic nerve

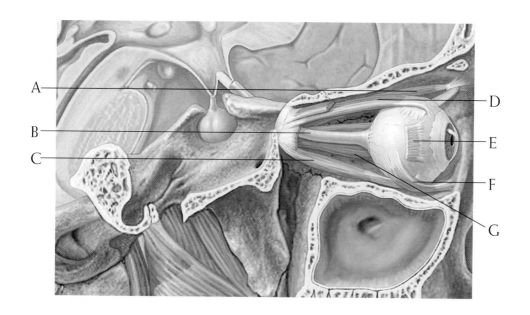

A. _____   E. _____

B. _____   F. _____

C. _____   G. _____

D. _____

11. External Ear

auricle / pinna   external acoustic (auditory) meatus
lobule   tragus

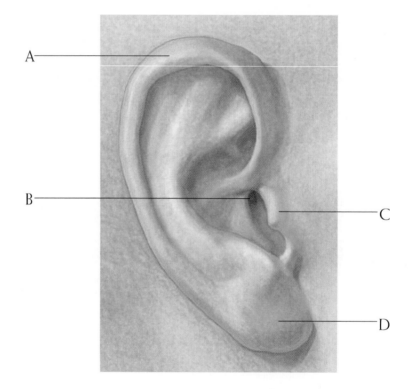

A. _____ C. _____

B. _____ D. _____

12. Inner Ear

semicircular canal   cochlea   vestibular nerve
vestibule   cochlear nerve

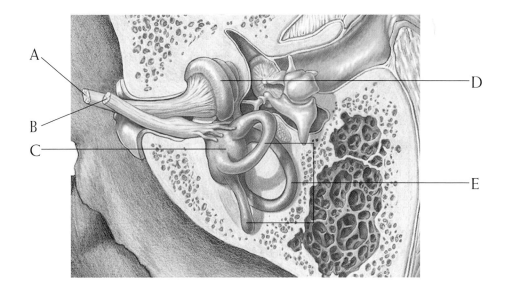

A. _____

B. _____

C. _____

D. _____

E. _____

13. Middle Ear

malleus

tympanic membrane

incus

stapes

external acoustic
(auditory) meatus

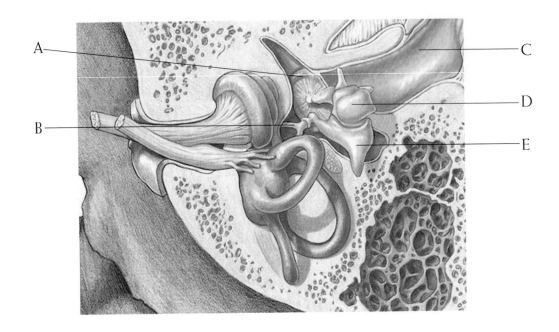

A. _____   D. _____

B. _____   E. _____

C. _____

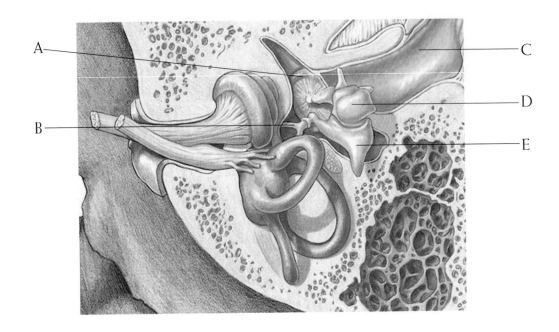

14. Eye

retina   palpebra   choroid   cornea

The inner, neural layer of the eye is known as the _____.

The middle, vascular layer of the eye is known as the _____.

The clear outer covering over the anterior surface of the eye is known as the

_____.

Another name for the eyelid is the _____.

15. Ear I

auricle   cochlea   middle   internal

The external, visible portion of the ear is known as the _____.

The region of the ear containing the ossicles is the _____ ear.

The region of the ear containing the sense organs for hearing and balance is
the _____ ear.

The portion of the ear containing the receptors for hearing is the

_____.

16. Ear II

tympanic membrane   semicircular canal   hammer
anvil   stirrup

The portion of the ear commonly referred to as the "ear drum" is the

_____.

The portion of the ear containing the receptors for dynamic balance is the

_____.

The _____ is the common name for the malleus.

The _____ is the common name for the incus.

The _____ is the common name for the stapes.

Write brief responses to the following scenarios.

1. Drugs known as beta blockers are so named because they bind to certain adrenergic (norepinephrine or epinephrine) receptors classified as beta type. When a beta blocker binds to a beta receptor, the beta receptor can no longer bind to epinephrine, effectively "blocking" the normal effects of this neurotransmitter's activity. What effect would such a drug have on cardiac activity?

2. Cocaine blocks the reuptake of catecholamines at the synaptic cleft. What effect would this have on the user's cardiovascular system?

3. A recent study presented at an American Heart Association meeting was the first to show scientific, quantitative data indicating that the use of pet therapy can help patients recover from heart failure. The data included measurements of patients' epinephrine levels. Do you think data supporting the use of pet therapy would show an increase or a decrease in the epinephrine levels of patients who were visited by dogs during their recovery? Why? Explain how this effect would aid in recovery from heart failure.

4. What are some possible physical abnormalities that might occur if a person has suffered damage to his or her brain stem? Discuss the possibilities in relation to the specific site of damage.

5. A new technique might make it possible to detect Alzheimer's disease before the neuron death associated with the disease occurs. Alzheimer's disease results from abnormal accumulation of the protein amyloid-beta 42 in brain tissue. Amyloid-beta 42 normally passes from the brain into the spinal fluid, where it is transferred to the blood and filtered out of

the body during excretion. The new technique involves monitoring spinal fluid for the presence of this protein. Into which category of disease would Alzheimer's be classified? How would the level of amyloid-beta 42 in the spinal fluid of a person in the beginning stages of Alzheimer's to compare with that of a person without the disease?

6. What abnormalities might be created by damage to each of the cerebral lobes?

7. To which of the two divisions of the forebrain might improper function of the pituitary gland be attributed, and what is the connection between this part of the brain and the endocrine system?

8. What type of sensory receptors most likely detect pheromones, and in which sensory organ(s) are they most likely located?

9. How could subarachnoid hemorrhaging could be detected?

10. What advantage does the blood-brain barrier provide for the body? What is a disadvantage that its presence creates in the treatment of certain diseases?

A.D.A.M. Education

Refer to the Encyclopedia section of A.D.A.M. Interactive Anatomy to open the A.D.A.M. Multimedia Encyclopedia. A quick search of key terms from the textbook will help you build on the knowledge you have gained thus far. Enter pathological terms such as *athetosis, chorea, neuroblastoma, stroke,* or *shaken baby syndrome* in the search bar to read more about these important topics that relate to the structure of the nervous system.

Laboratory Activity 1

The Stroop Effect and Brain Function

Background

The brain is responsible for combining information from all the senses into organized thoughts that lead to appropriate responses to incoming stimuli. In this activity, you will test a brain function phenomenon called the Stroop effect, which is a form of neural interaction called *interference*. Interference occurs when information from one nerve tract or nervous system function obstructs the action or impulses of another neural pathway. Dr. John Ridley Stroop wrote a medical study on brain function interference in 1935. He discovered that the ability to make an appropriate response is impaired when a subject is presented with two conflicting signals. This impairment is known today as "the Stroop effect." The interference occurs in an area of the brain called the anterior cingulate, which is located in a region of the brain between the right and left halves of the frontal lobe. The anterior cingulate helps organize emotional responses and learned thought processes. The lab activity that follows is one way to measure the Stroop effect.

Materials

- Lab partner
- Lists in Figure 9.1 (or alternate lists)
- Stopwatch or clock with a second hand
- Paper for recording individual student results
- Board or projector for showing class data

Procedure

In this activity, you and your lab partner will take turns being timed as you recite the colors of the words in the lists in Figure 9.1. You must say the colors aloud as fast as possible with as few errors as possible. Designate one person as Person A and one person as Person B, and follow the steps below to complete the activity:

1. Person A gets the stopwatch or clock ready to time Trial 1.
2. Person A says "go," and Person B says the color of the words (not the words themselves) in List 1 out loud.
3. Person A records how long it took Person B to read the list.
4. Repeat steps 1 through 3 three more times (for a total of four times) and record the average.
5. Repeat steps 1 through 4 for List 2.
6. Repeat steps 1 through 4 for List 3.
7. Repeat steps 1 through 6 with Person A saying the colors and Person B timing and recording.
8. Record all of your data in a chart so that you can compare it with your classmates' results.

Figure 9.1

List 1	List 2	List 3
RED	YELLOW	Word
YELLOW	GREEN	Word
GREEN	BLUE	Word
BLUE	RED	Word
RED	BLUE	Word
BLUE	YELLOW	Word
YELLOW	GREEN	Word
GREEN	BLUE	Word
BLUE	RED	Word
RED	YELLOW	Word

Analysis

Analyze the results of this activity by responding to the following questions:

1. Were there any differences in the times it took to say the colors in each list?
2. What factors interfered with the ability to quickly say the name of the color?
3. Is there evidence that it is more difficult to name the color of the word when the word doesn't match its color?
4. Were there any differences between you and your partner in the time it took to name the colors in List 2? If so, what are some possible explanations for these differences?

Laboratory Activity 2

Brain Pathology Interpretation

Background

Many diseases cause visible changes to the brain's structure. These changes are easily identifiable under a microscope. This laboratory activity requires you to compare human brain tissue with that of a diseased sheep. Images 1 and 2 are sections of a sheep brain with a disease called transmissible spongiform encephalopathy (TSE), or scrapie. Scrapie is caused by prions and is related to mad cow disease and Creutzfeldt-Jakob disease. Humans usually cannot contract scrapie. However, it is possible to get related diseases from cattle, horses, and pigs. More information, including images of Creutzfeldt-Jakob disease, can be found at http://anatphys.emcp.net/NINDS_cjd.

Materials

- Microscope with high-power capability (400X)
- Prepared slide of human brain

Procedure and Analysis

Place the prepared slide of the human brain under the microscope. Start with the low magnification, and move to the higher magnification to see details and individual cells. Can you distinguish between the nerve cell bodies, axons, and neuroglia? How many nerve cell bodies can be seen in the viewing field? Does the number vary from one part of the brain to another?

Now, look at the microscopic photographs below and answer the questions for each image.

Figure 9.2

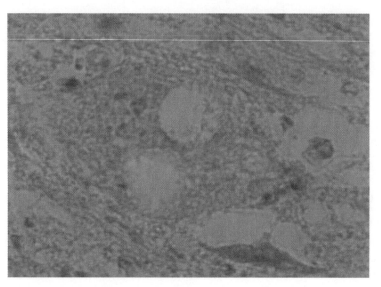

1. How does the brain specimen in Figure 9.2 differ from normal brain tissue?
2. How would you explain the large, round, dark cells?
3. Are the small, irregular holes found in normal brain tissue? What might these holes indicate?

Figure 9.3

1. How does the brain specimen in Figure 9.3 differ from normal brain tissue?
2. How does it differ from Figure 9.2?
3. Explain the presence of the brown "stringy" cells in this brain specimen.

Quiz

1. Information from the CNS is carried to muscles or glands by:
   a) sensory neurons
   b) afferent neurons
   c) motor neurons
   d) All of the above

2. Which of the following describes the endoneurium?
   a) It separates nerve cells from one another.
   b) It surrounds axons and myelin.
   c) It maintains selectivity of what enters and exits axons.
   d) All of the above

3. Ganglia of the central nervous system:
   a) are anatomically identical to those of the peripheral nervous system
   b) usually have a motor function
   c) would not have Nodes of Ranvier as part of their anatomy
   d) All of the above

4. Which of the following describes the meninges?
   a) They separate the brain from the skull, and the spinal cord from the vertebrae.
   b) They consist of three distinct layers.
   c) They are associated with ependymal cells for cerebrospinal fluid production.
   d) All of the above

5. Gray matter is composed mainly of _____ and is located _____ in the spinal cord.
   a) neurons/centrally
   b) axons/centrally
   c) neurons/peripherally
   d) axons/peripherally

6. Basal nuclei in the brain:
   a) function for memory
   b) function for body movement
   c) relay sensory information to the brain
   d) control emotion

7. Which of the following statements is true of the cerebral hemispheres?
   a) Both are involved equally in determining an individual's behavior.
   b) Specialized regions for speech and language are present in the right hemisphere.
   c) Dominance of the right hemisphere is associated with artistic talent.
   d) All of the above

8. Damage to the temporal lobe might affect the ability to:
   a) move your legs
   b) focus your eyes correctly
   c) feel hunger
   d) recognize a friend's voice

9. The ventricles of the central nervous system:
   a) are isolated cavities within the brain
   b) circulate cerebrospinal fluid
   c) provide space for air circulation in the brain
   d) All of the above

10. The portion of the brain that plays a major role in autonomic control of breathing and cardiovascular function is the:
    a) medulla oblongata
    b) pons
    c) midbrain
    d) diencephalon

11. A person with degeneration of the cerebellum would most likely experience loss of:
    a) vision
    b) memory
    c) balance
    d) All of the above

12. Ascending nerve tracts:
    a) carry sensory information
    b) carry motor information
    c) are located ventrally in the spinal column
    d) All of the above

13. The cranial nerves are:
    a) part of the central nervous system
    b) part of the peripheral nervous system
    c) surrounded by the meninges and cerebrospinal fluid
    d) solely sensory in function

14. Dorsal root ganglia:
    a) have ascending axons
    b) are located in the ventral horn of gray matter
    c) have motor function
    d) All of the above

15. Which of the following is true about the arrangement of neurons in the autonomic nervous system?
    a) Preganglionic neurons are myelinated, while postganglionic neurons are not.
    b) Preganglionic neurons of the parasympathetic nervous system are longer than postganglionic neurons.
    c) Preganglionic neurons of the sympathetic nervous system are shorter than postganglionic neurons.
    d) All of the above

16. In the autonomic nervous system, postganglionic neurons:
    a) of the parasympathetic system always innervate effectors that are different than those of the sympathetic system
    b) of both the parasympathetic and sympathetic systems secrete the same neurotransmitters
    c) of the sympathetic system secrete norepinephrine
    d) All of the above

17. Acetylcholine is the neurotransmitter secreted by:
    a) parasympathetic postganglionic neurons
    b) preganglionic neurons of both sympathetic and parasympathetic neurons
    c) neurons causing skeletal muscle contraction
    d) All of the above

18. Which of the following statements is true regarding sympathetic nerve activity?
    a) It is always excitatory.
    b) It is always inhibitory.
    c) It is excitatory to some receptors and inhibitory to others.
    d) It is only excitatory to skeletal muscles.

19. Which of the following is a correct pathway for sound transmission?
    a) external auditory meatus, tympanic membrane, malleus, incus, stapes, oval window, round window
    b) auricle, tympanic membrane, incus, malleus, stapes, oval window, round window
    c) tympanic membrane, malleus, incus, stapes, round window, oval window
    d) oval window, tympanic membrane, malleus, incus stapes, round window

20. Whiplash is an example of a(n):
    a) cerebrovascular disease
    b) traumatic neuropathy
    c) arteriovenous malformation
    d) neurodegenerative disease

21. Aneurysms, arteriovenous malformations, and ischemic attacks are all examples of:
    a) neurodegenerative disease
    b) traumatic neuropathy
    c) effects of aging
    d) vascular anomalies

22. Which of the following nervous system disorders is the result of abnormal dopamine production?
    a) chorea
    b) palsy
    c) athetosis
    d) All of the above

23. Decreased function of sensory perception in elderly persons is most likely attributed to:
    a) the extreme loss of neurons that accompanies aging
    b) plasticity and/or redundancy
    c) degradation of the sensory structures
    d) All of the above

24. Plasticity and redundancy:
    a) are compensatory mechanisms of aging
    b) have a direct correlation with dendrite number
    c) are increased by regular mental and physical activity throughout a person's lifetime
    d) All of the above

25. Match the letter of each of the following terms with the corresponding sense and/or body structure. Letters may be used more than once.

    a) audition
    b) equilibrium
    c) gustation
    d) olfaction
    e) vision

    _____ conjunctiva
    _____ tympanic membrane
    _____ chemoreceptors
    _____ ciliary body
    _____ smell
    _____ sclera
    _____ taste buds
    _____ retina
    _____ lacrimalx
    _____ eustachian tube
    _____ cochlea
    _____ vestibule

CHAPTER

10

THE RESPIRATORY SYSTEM

Introduction

The body requires a constant supply of oxygen and nutrients to maintain homeo-stasis, as well as a route for the excretion of metabolic waste products to prevent a toxic buildup in the bloodstream. The respiratory system is responsible for deliver-ing oxygen to the body and removing carbon dioxide from the blood through a process known as respiration. The following exercises require you to apply what you have learned about the respiratory system. Refer to Chapter 10 of *Applied Anatomy & Physiology, A Case Study Approach* if you need assistance. Access A.D.A.M. Interactive Anatomy for additional information and to deepen your understanding of the con-cepts presented in the textbook.

Completion

Complete the following sentences by filling in each blank with a key term from the text.

1. The part of the respiratory system that contains the nose, nasal cavity, paranasal sinuses, eustachian tubes, and larynx is the _____ _____ sys-tem, while the trachea, bronchial tree, and lungs are part of the _____ _____ system.

2. The network of passages that supply the lungs with air is called the _____ _____. It is composed of the right and left _____, which continually branch to form _____ _____, _____ _____, _____, and _____ _____.

3. The upper part of the throat behind the nose is referred to as the _____; it contains the immune system structures called _____, while the part of the throat just inferior is called the _____ and con-tains the immune system structures known as the _____.

4. The three major cartilages that form the larynx are the _____, _____, and _____.

5. The _____ is the serous membrane of the lungs; it consists of the inner _____ layer and the outer _____ layer.

6. Breathing is often referred to as _____, further differentiated as either _____, which describes the mechanical process of breathing, or _____, which means the exchange of oxygen and carbon dioxide between the blood and body cells.

7. Air movement into the lungs, known as _____, occurs when the diaphragm _____. _____, or movement of air out of the lungs, occurs when the diaphragm _____.

8. Inflammation caused by infection in only one lobe of the lung is called _____ _____, but widespread, infectious inflammation is called _____.

9. A common viral disease spread through respiratory fluids is _____. A rare viral respiratory disease that can be contracted through rodent contact is _____ _____ _____ (_____).

10. The maximum quantity of air the lungs can hold after forced breathing is a measurement called _____ _____ _____; it is the sum of the measurements of _____ _____ and _____ _____.

Matching

Match each of the following terms with the corresponding description by writing the letter of the term on the blank next to the correct description.

a) atelectasis

b) bronchodilation

c) diaphragm

d) emphysema

e) Heimlich maneuver

f) intrapleural pressure

g) laryngeal prominence

h) larynx

i) lobule

j) nares

k) pharynx

l) restrictive lung disease

m) tidal volume

n) ventilation

o) vomeronasal gland

_____ caused by damage to the alveoli

_____ used to alleviate choking

_____ nostrils

_____ throat

_____ prevents lung collapse

_____ contains chemoreceptors

_____ voice box

_____ inadequate lung expansion

_____ lung collapse

_____ breathing

_____ Adam's apple

_____ respiratory passage enlargement

_____ breathing muscle

_____ amount of air in a normal breath

_____ subdivision of the lungs

Complete the Terms Table

Fill in the missing key terms and/or definitions in the following table.

Term	Definition
	air cavities within the facial bones
trachea	
epiglottis	
	the constriction of smooth-muscle bands in the terminal bronchioles
alveolus	
partial pressure	
	the abnormal stretching and dilation of the bronchi or bronchioles
	a lung infection caused by the inactive stage of a worm
Acute Respiratory Distress Syndrome (ARDS)	
	the amount of air moved into and out of the lungs in one minute
inspiratory reserve volume	
	the amount of air that is forcefully expired after a normal exhalation

Label the Graphic

Identify each of the following terms in the illustration on the following page. Write the number of the respiratory system part in the box indicating its location. Then answer the questions that follow.

1. alveolar duct
2. alveolar sac
3. alveoli
4. bronchioles
5. capillary
6. laryngopharynx
7. larynx
8. left and right primary bronchi
9. lower respiratory tract
10. lungs
11. nasal cavity
12. nasopharynx
13. oropharynx
14. trachea
15. upper respiratory tract

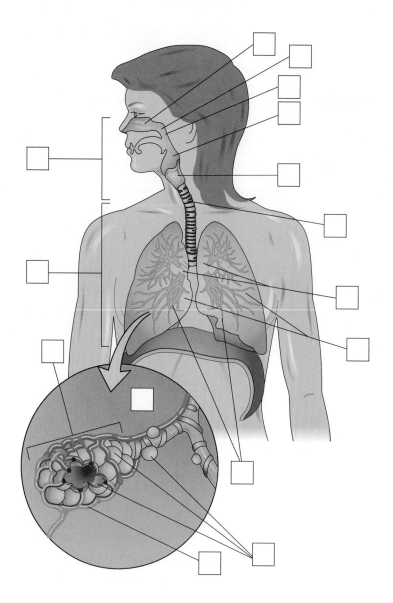

1. Beginning with the nasal cavity, the lining of the respiratory tract has special hairlike structures and a layer of a substance secreted by the epithelial cells. What are the names of these two components of the tract lining, and what purpose do they serve?

2. Where does gas exchange between the air and lungs actually take place?

3. Why does the left lung have a notch at its inferior medial end?

Color the Graphic

Color this illustration using the following color key:

adenoids – light green

parnasal sinuses – brown

tonsils – dark green

nasopharynx – yellow

oropharynx – orange

laryngopharynx – red

epiglottis – light blue

thyroid cartilage – dark blue

vocal cords – black

trachea – pink

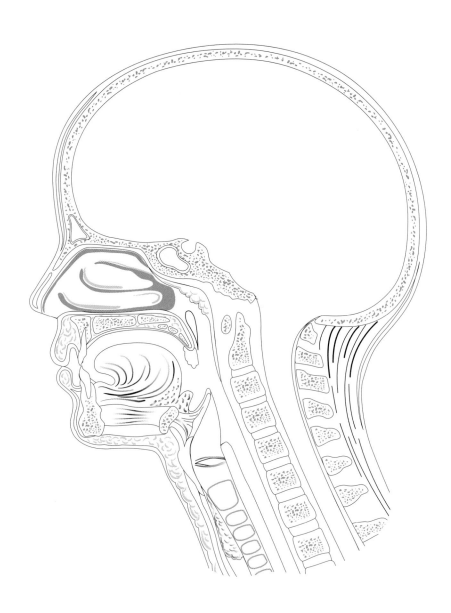

✿A.D.A.M. Education

To view an animated presentation of the respiratory system, click on the Clinical Animations tab within A.D.A.M. Interactive Anatomy. Refine your search by choosing *Respiratory* from the Body System menu, clicking the search button, and then choosing the *Gas exchange* animation.

Additional Practice: The Respiratory System

Identify the location of each of the terms listed above the image. Write the name of the body part on the corresponding line beneath the image.

1. Thorax (Lat)

diaphragm   pericardial sac   trachea
right primary bronchus   superior vena cava

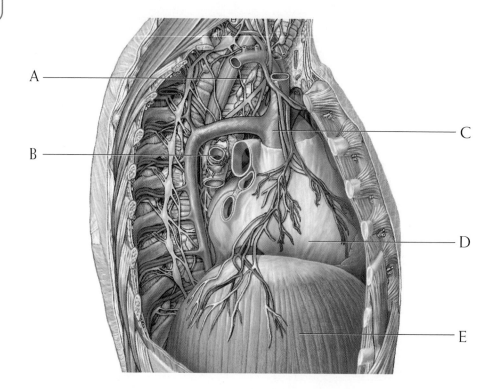

A. _____   D. _____

B. _____   E. _____

C. _____

2. Nasal Cavity (Med)

nostril
frontal sinus
pharyngeal tonsil /
   adenoids

inferior nasal concha
superior nasal concha
auditory tube /
   Eustachian tube

middle nasal concha
sphenoidal sinus

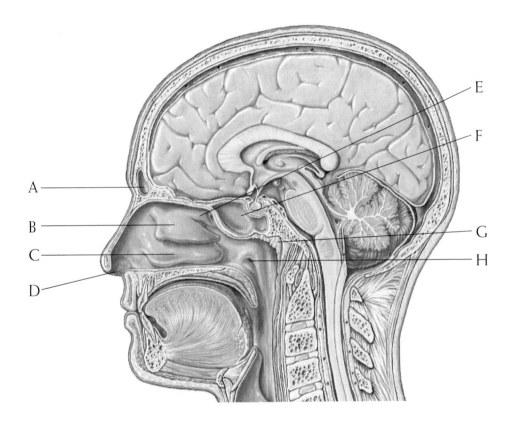

A. _____

B. _____

C. _____

D. _____

E. _____

F. _____

G. _____

H. _____

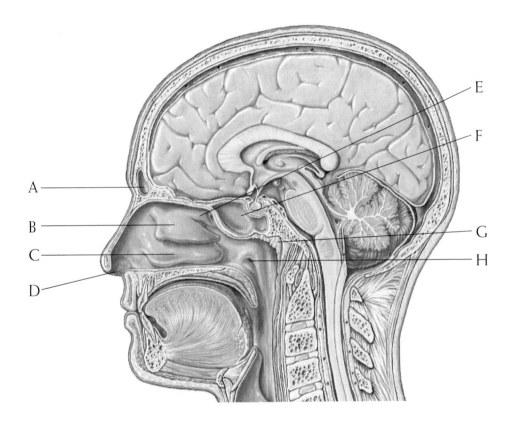ADAM.Education

3. Pharynx (Med)

nasopharynx   oropharynx   laryngopharynx
cricoid cartilage esophagus   trachea
thyroid cartilage epiglottis

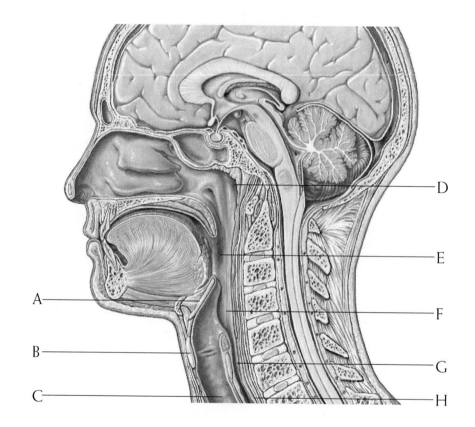

A. _____ E. _____

B. _____ F. _____

C. _____ G. _____

D. _____ H. _____

4. Larynx (Ant)

epiglottis   hyoid bone   laryngeal prominence /Adam's apple
thyroid cartilage   cricoid cartilage   trachea

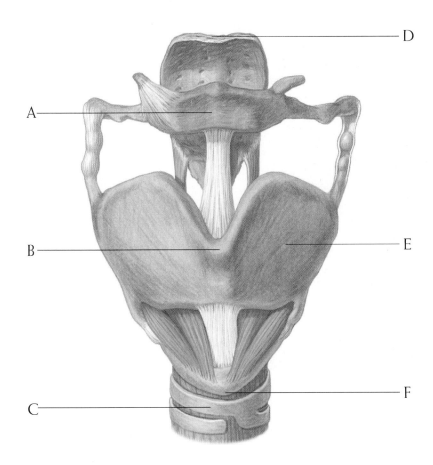

A. _____   D. _____

B. _____   E. _____

C. _____   F. _____

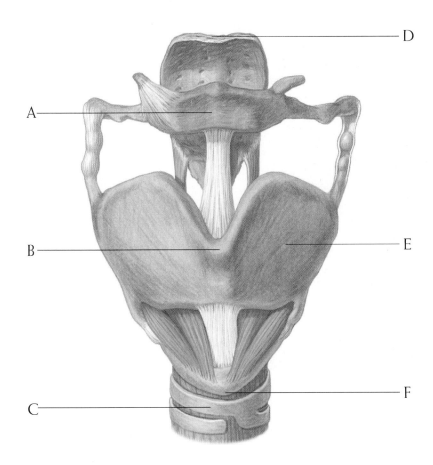A.D.A.M.Education

5. Larynx (Post)

hyoid bone   tracheal cartilage   arytenoid cartilage
thyroid cartilage   epiglottis   cricoid cartilage

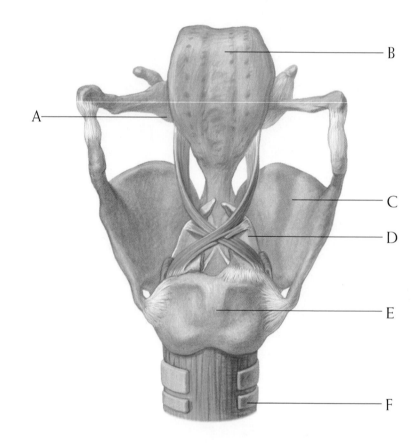

A. _____ D. _____

B. _____ E. _____

C. _____ F. _____

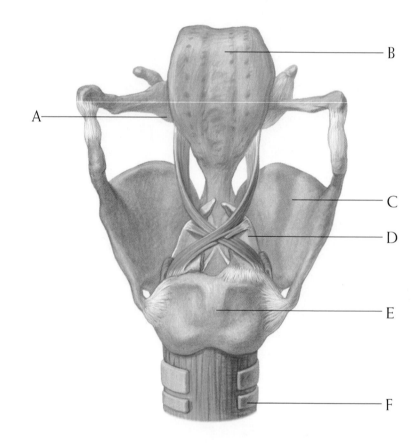

6. Lungs

left superior lobe   left oblique fissue   left inferior lobe
right inferior lobe   right oblique fissure   right middle lobe
right horizontal fissure   right superior lobe

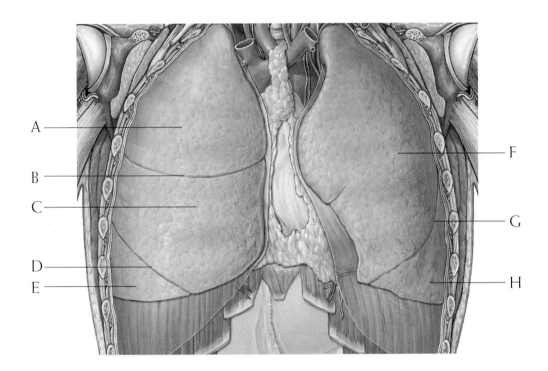

A. _____   E. _____

B. _____   F. _____

C. _____   G. _____

D. _____   H. _____

7. Frontal Bronchi

epiglottis   cricoid cartilage   trachea
left primary bronchus   esophagus   right primary bronchus
thyroid cartilage   hyoid bone

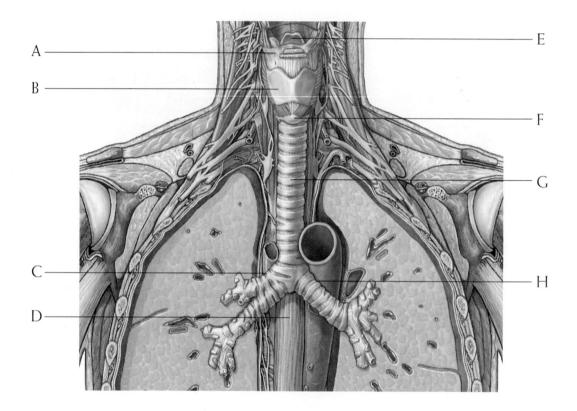

A. _____   E. _____

B. _____   F. _____

C. _____   G. _____

D. _____   H. _____

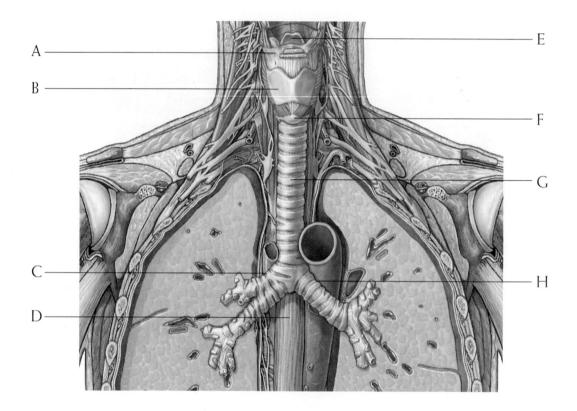

8. Pulmonary Ventilation

ventilation   tidal   external   internal

The movement of air into and out of the lungs is called _____.

The exchange of gases between the alveoli of the lungs and the blood is called _____ respiration.

The exchange of gases between the blood and tissues is called _____respiration.

The amount of air exchanged during quiet, restful breathing is called _____volume.

9. Respiratory Volumes

inhalation   emphysema   exhalation   asthma

The active phase of breathing, drawing air into the lungs is called

_____.

The passive phase of breathing when air leaves the lungs is called

_____.

The disease characterized by narrow respiratory passageways obstructing the movement of air into and out of the lungs is called _____.

The disease characterized by a reduction in the number of alveoli and a loss of elasticity of lung tissue is called _____.

A.D.A.M. Education

For additional information on common conditions associated with the respiratory system, click on the Clinical Illustrations tab in A.D.A.M. Interactive Anatomy. Narrow your search by choosing *Respiratory* from the Body System menu. A quick search will lead you to a variety of images to explore including the lungs, bronchitis, emphysema, the pleural cavity, smoker's lung, asthma, and lung cancer.

Practical Application

Write brief responses to the following scenarios.

1. Cigarette smoking causes the movement of the cilia lining the respiratory tract to cease. What connection does this have with the chronic cough that many smokers experience?

2. Cystic fibrosis is a genetic disease that causes a drastic increase in the amount of mucus produced in the body. This can cause the bronchioles to become blocked. What type of damage would probably occur as a result of blocked bronchioles, and what is the term used to describe this condition?

3. Why might someone experience soreness in his or her chest following heavy aerobic exercise? Which specific locations are most likely to feel sore?

4. Breathing is under the involuntary control of the nervous system. When carbon dioxide builds up in the blood, it results in an increase in hydrogen ions. The brain detects this increase and communicates the need to increase the rate and depth of breathing. What type of receptors would detect this stimulus? What specific division of the nervous system would be involved in the response to the stimulus? What would be the effectors in the reflex arc? What could a runner voluntarily do to help keep the need to increase his or her breathing rate to a minimum?

5. What effect would breathing into a paper bag have on the partial pressure of oxygen and carbon dioxide in the blood versus the atmosphere?

6. How might a knife wound to the thorax interrupt mechanical breathing, even if it were not deep enough to actually enter the lung?

7. Describe the anatomical features of the lungs that prevent damage in one location from having a detrimental effect on the entire lung.

8. Which division of the nervous system is activated by drugs used to treat asthma?

9. Although about 30% of the carbon dioxide in the blood is transported by binding to red blood cells, the majority of these molecules are converted to a compound called carbonic acid. Carbonic acid quickly dissociates into bicarbonate ions and hydrogen ions. How is this significant to the respiratory system's role in maintaining homeostasis in the body? Give an example of another body system that could be affected if the respiratory system did not carry out this function.

10. While you are having dinner with a friend, a woman at the next table appears to be having trouble swallowing and clearly tells you that she thinks she is choking. Should you consider performing the Heimlich maneuver?

Laboratory Activity 1

Histology of Lung Pathology

Background

Histologists and pathologists look at microscopic preparations of lung tissue to better understand respiratory diseases. They compare slides of normal lung tissue with slides of diseased lung tissue to gain experience determining the different components and cell types in the respiratory system. This laboratory activity will allow you to practice this same type of comparison by analyzing normal lung tissue and images of diseased lung tissue.

Materials

- Microscope with high-power capability (400X)
- Prepared slide of a normal human lung

Procedure and Analysis

Place the slide of the normal human lung under the microscope. Start with low magnification and move to higher magnification to see details and individual cells. Now, compare the slide findings with the diseased lung specimens on the Urbana Atlas of Pathology website at http://anatphys.emcp.net/UrbanaAtlasPath. Analyze your findings by answering the following questions:

1. Can you find the terminal bronchioles and the alveoli? What do they look like?
2. What are the similarities and differences between the normal lung and each diseased lung?
3. How does each disease affect the histological appearance of the lung?

Laboratory Activity 2

Lung Function Models (Part 1): Lung Capacity Model

Background

Physicians and scientists regularly use biological models to better understand body functions. Biological models are representations of body functions. In this activity, you will learn about human lung capacity by building a model for measuring the amount of air displaced by the lung during expiration.

Materials

- Empty 1-gallon milk jug with a cap
- Metric measuring cup or beaker
- Masking tape
- Black, fine-point permanent marker
- Water
- 1 meter (about 3 feet) of aquarium tubing
- Large, flat-bottomed baking pan that can hold 1 gallon of water

Procedure

1. Place a strip of masking tape down the side of the milk jug from the top to the bottom.
2. Fill the jug with water, using the measuring cup or beaker to add one liter at a time. Mark the level of the water on the tape after you add each liter.
3. Place the cap on the jug.
4. Fill the baking pan about half full with water.
5. Slowly place the jug upside down in the water and remove the cap after the mouth of the jug is submerged. Do not allow air bubbles to enter the milk jug.
6. Lift the jug carefully, making sure the opening stays submerged, and place one end of the aquarium tubing inside the mouth of the jug. Make sure there are at least 3 inches of tubing inside the jug.
7. Take a normal breath, and exhale into the tubing. The volume of air entering the jug should displace the same volume of water. Mark the water level on the tape. Record the data.
8. Refill the jug with water and return it to the baking pan.
9. Breathe in deeply and make an effort to exhale all of the air in your lungs through the tubing. Mark the water level on the tape, and record the data.
10. Repeat steps 7 and 8 three times. Find the average of the readings. If others will be sharing the same setup, replace the tubing before they use it.

Analysis

Compare your data with your classmates' data. Create a brief analysis in the form of a report, PowerPoint presentation, or chart.

Laboratory Activity 3

Lung Function Models (Part 2): Inspiration and Expiration Model

Background

The biological model you will create in this activity represents the action of the diaphragm in human respiration. It can be adapted to model the way certain respiratory diseases affect inspiration and expiration.

Materials

- Soda straw cut into 2-inch lengths
- Scissors
- Two small, round party balloons
- One large, round party balloon
- Fast-drying glue
- Large, clear plastic cup
- Two small rubber bands
- A rubber band large enough to just fit over the lip of the cup
- Clear tape

Procedure

1. Take a 2-inch section of straw and cut a small triangle in the center. Make sure you do not cut through to the opposite side
2. Place one small balloon over each end of the straw and secure them with the small rubber bands. Test the setup to make sure that both balloons begin to fill when air is blown into the straw through the triangular opening.
3. Bend the straw in the middle of the hole so that the opening is facing up.
4. Take another 2-inch piece of straw and cut a V-shape on one end. Fit the slanted points of the straw into the opening of the hole on the bent straw.
5. Apply glue to hold the two pieces of straw together and allow it to dry. The structure you have created is called the lung model. The straight straw is the trachea, and the bent straw serves as the bronchi that lead to each lung (balloon).
6. Cut a hole in the bottom of the clear plastic cup, using the diameter of the straw as a guide to the size.
7. Push the trachea of the lung model (the straight straw) into the hole of the plastic cup from the inside. Glue the trachea in place in the hole. The cup should now be upside down with the trachea holding the lungs within the cup.
8. Take your large balloon and cut off the neck. Carefully stretch the cut balloon over the opening of the cup, taking care not to crack the cup. Secure the edges of the balloon with the large rubber band. This balloon represents the diaphragm.
9. Now, pull the bottom balloon gently, and observe what happens.
10. Place one finger just above the trachea and repeat step 9. Observe what happens to the model.
11. Slowly release the bottom balloon and observe what happens.
12. Place one finger just above the trachea, and repeat step 11. Observe what happens.
13. How does this model represent the role of the diaphragm in inspiration and expiration?
14. Rebuild the setup with a piece of tape on one of the small balloons. Observe what happens when you model the action of the diaphragm.
15. Poke a hole in one of the small balloons and rebuild the setup . Observe what happens when you model the action of the diaphragm.

Analysis

1. Describe what happened to the flow of air through the trachea in step 9 (pulling the bottom balloon).
2. Describe what happened to the flow of air through the trachea in step 11 (releasing the bottom of the balloon).
3. How does the lung model illustrate the role of the diaphragm in inspiration and expiration?
4. What disease is represented by the modifications you made to the model in step 14?
5. What disease is represented by the modifications you made to the model in step 15?

Quiz

1. The exchange of gas between the respiratory and circulatory systems occurs by:
   a) active transport
   b) osmosis
   c) passive diffusion
   d) All of the above

2. Which of the following respiratory components is considered by some to be part of the upper respiratory tract, but is considered part of the lower respiratory tract by others?
   a) eustachian tube
   b) pharynx
   c) trachea
   d) larynx

3. The purpose of the large number of blood vessels in the nasal cavity is to:
   a) moisten the air
   b) warm the air
   c) transfer gases
   d) remove foreign material

4. Many hypothesize that the purpose of the paranasal cavities is to:
   a) protect the skull
   b) create speech resonance
   c) warm and moisten inhaled air
   d) both b and c

5. Of what other body system is the pharynx also a component?
   a) the lymphatic system
   b) the muscular system
   c) the digestive system
   d) the endocrine system

6. Incomplete closure of which structure can allow food to accidentally enter the respiratory passages?
   a) epiglottis
   b) thyroid cartilage
   c) larynx
   d) glottis

7. The vocal cords are muscles housed by the _____ and held in place by the _____.
   a) pharynx/cricoid cartilage
   b) larynx/epiglottis
   c) pharynx/arytenoid cartilage
   d) larynx/arytenoid cartilage

8. Which of the following best describes the trachea?
   a) It contains continuous tracheal cartilages.
   b) It is anterior to the esophagus.
   c) It functions as a passage for food.
   d) All of the above

9. Which of the following describes the bronchioles?
   a) They are smaller than the bronchi.
   b) They contain no cartilage.
   c) They are larger than the terminal bronchioles.
   d) All of the above

10. Sympathetic nerve innervation would _____ air intake by _____.
    a) increase/bronchodilation
    b) increase/bronchoconstriction
    c) decrease/bronchocontriction
    d) decrease/bronchodilation

11. Damage in one area of the lung:
    a) prevents the proper function of the complete organ
    b) is usually a life-threatening condition
    c) affects all lobes
    d) is localized by the independent functioning of lobes and lobules

12. Which of the following describes the action of surfactant in the lungs?
    a) It catalyzes gas exchange.
    b) It engulfs microbes.
    c) It prevents evaporation and alveolar collapse.
    d) All of the above

13. Where in the lungs does gas exchange occur?
    a) in the alveoli
    b) in the respiratory portion of the lobules
    c) across epithelial cells
    d) All of the above

14. Oxygen and carbon dioxide gas exchange:
    a) always occurs as a result of breathing
    b) depends on the partial pressures of each gas
    c) is often referred to as external respiration
    d) All of the above

15. Breathing is under _____ control.
    a) involuntary
    b) voluntary
    c) sympathetic and parasympathetic
    d) All of the above

16. When the diaphragm contracts, it:
    a) forces air out of the lungs
    b) lowers
    c) increases the internal pressure of the lungs
    d) All of the above

17. Air moves into the lungs due to:
    a) a decrease in lung volume
    b) an increase in the thoracic-cavity pressure
    c) a decrease in the thoracic-cavity pressure
    d) relaxation of the diaphragm

18. Relaxation of the diaphragm causes:
    a) a decrease in lung volume
    b) an increase in thoracic pressure
    c) upward movement of the diaphragm
    d) All of the above

19. The difference in gas levels between the air in the alveoli and the alveolar capillary blood:
    a) controls the measurement known as partial pressure
    b) controls mechanical breathing
    c) establishes active transport measures
    d) All of the above

20. If the partial pressure of a gas is higher in the blood than in the atmosphere, that gas:
    a) will remain in the blood
    b) will leave the blood
    c) is present in a higher concentration in the atmosphere
    d) will not diffuse across the alveolar membrane

21. How does the partial pressure of carbon dioxide in the blood entering the alveoli normally compare with the atmospheric partial pressure of carbon dioxide?
    a) It is higher.
    b) It is lower.
    c) It is equivalent.
    d) It consistently fluctuates from higher to lower.

22. Atelectasis could result from:
    a) chronic obstructive pulmonary disease (COPD)
    b) pneumothorax
    c) lung cancer
    d) All of the above

23. Which of the following could result in bronchiectasis?
    a) asthma
    b) bronchitis
    c) long-term accumulation of mucus
    d) All of the above

24. Which of the following is an example of an infectious respiratory disease?
    a) tuberculosis
    b) pneumonia
    c) influenza
    d) All of the above

25. Which of the following measurements of lung capacity reflects the fact that the lungs are never totally empty of air?
    a) tidal volume
    b) vital capacity
    c) residual volume
    d) expiratory reserve volume

CHAPTER

THE CARDIOVASCULAR SYSTEM

Introduction

The cardiovascular system consists of the heart, which serves as a pump, and a vast network of blood vessels designed to supply nutrient-rich blood to all parts of the body. Pulmonary circulation delivers blood to the lungs, where it becomes oxygenated, and systemic circulation delivers oxygenated blood to the body tissues. The following exercises and lab activities will help you apply what you have learned about the cardiovascular system and its role in maintaining homeostasis. When completing the activities in this chapter, refer to Chapter 11 of *Applied Anatomy & Physiology, A Case Study Approach* for assistance, if necessary. Access A.D.A.M. Interactive Anatomy for additional information and opportunities to deepen your understanding of the concepts presented in the textbook.

Completion

Complete the following sentences by filling in each blank with a key term from the text.

1. _____ is a term used to describe the development and growth of blood vessels. It is directed by chemicals called _____ _____.

2. The three major types of vessels that transport blood are _____, _____, and _____.

3. Arteries and veins have three distinct layers: the inner _____ _____, middle _____ _____, and outer _____ _____.

4. The _____ side of the heart pumps blood to the body, which is known as _____ circulation, and the _____ side pumps blood to the _____, or into _____ circulation.

5. _____ _____, or lack of oxygen in the heart, can cause the heart to function abnormally and can lead to muscle cell death and/or _____ _____, if severe enough.

6. The valves separating the upper and lower heart chambers are the
   _____ valves; the one on the left is the _____ valve,
   and the one on the right is the _____ valve. The valves separating each ventricle from the blood vessels that leave the heart are the
   _____ valves.

7. The heart's electrical conduction is initiated by the _____
   _____, and continues in a specific order to the _____
   _____, the _____ ____ _____ , and the
   _____ _____.

8. In the fetal heart, an opening between the right and left atria called the
   _____ _____ and a blood vessel between the pulmonary
   artery and the aorta called the _____ _____ allow blood
   to bypass the lungs.

9. One complete contraction and relaxation of the heart is called the
   _____ _____. It consists of two stages: 1) _____,
   which is heart muscle relaxation and ventricular filling; and 2)
   _____, which is ventricular contraction and ejection of blood.

10. The medical terms for the progressive narrowing and hardening of arteries
    due to _____ formation are often differentiated as _____,
    which results from fat deposits, and _____, which results from
    calcium deposits.

Matching

Match each of the following terms with the corresponding description by
placing the letter of the term on the blank next to the correct description.

a) aneurysm

b) aorta

c) atrium

d) cardiac output

e) coronary artery

f) epicardium

g) fibrillation

h) myocardium

i) prolapse

j) pulmonary artery

k) SA node

l) thrombosis

m) vasoconstriction

n) ventricle

o) venules

_____ pericardial visceral layer

_____ blood clot

_____ bulge in a blood vessel

_____ upper heart chamber

_____ rapid cardiac muscle contraction

_____ narrowing of the blood vessels

_____ vein branch

_____ the amount of blood pumped by the
         heart each minute

_____ exits the left ventricle

_____ lower heart chamber

_____ stretched heart valve

_____ starts the heart beat

_____ exits the right ventricle

_____ cardiac muscle

_____ supplies blood to the heart muscle

Complete the Terms Table

Complete the missing key terms and/or definitions in the following table.

Term	Definition
	the widening of the diameter of a blood vessel
pericardium	
	specialized muscle cells that carry the electric impulses through the ventricles
papillary muscles	
venae cavae	
	the amount of blood the ventricle of the heart pumps with each beat
electrocardiography	
	the portion of an electrocardiogram that represents ventricular depolarization and contraction
	chest pain due to coronary heart disease
endocarditis	
	irregular rhythmic beating of the heart
	a condition in which the heart cannot pump out all of the blood that enters the chambers
	heart valve damage due to *Streptococcus* bacterial infection
cardiovagal baroreflex	
sudden cardiac death	

Label the Graphic

Identify each of the terms in the illustration on the next page. Write the number of the cardiac part in the box indicating its location, and then answer the questions that follow.

1. aorta
2. aortic semilunar valve
3. bicuspid valve
4. chordae tendinae
5. inferior vena cava
6. interventricular septum
7. left atrium
8. left ventricle
9. pulmonary arteries
10. pulmonary semilunar valve
11. pulmonary veins
12. right atrium
13. right ventricle
14. superior vena cava
15. tricuspid valve

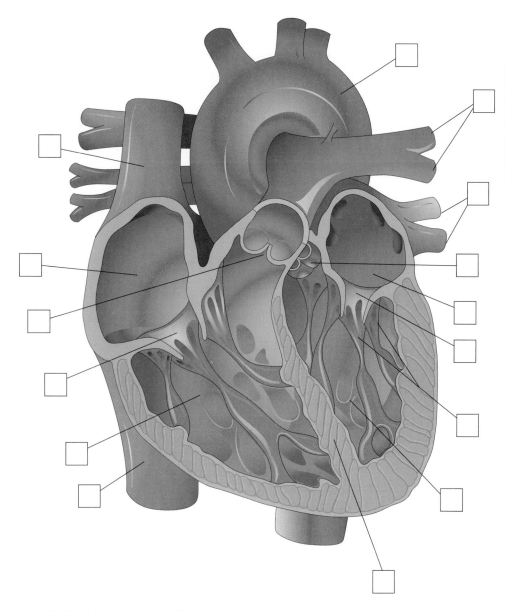

1. Is the blood in the pulmonary arteries high or low in oxygen content?

2. Which side of the heart sends blood into systemic circulation?

3. Which side of the heart receives blood from pulmonary circulation?

4. Which side of the heart receives blood that is low in oxygen content?

Color the Graphic

Color the illustration using the following color key:

superior vena cava – red   left ventricle – purple
right atrium – pink   inferior vena cava – brown
left atrium – green   interventricular septum – blue
right ventricle – yellow   aorta – orange

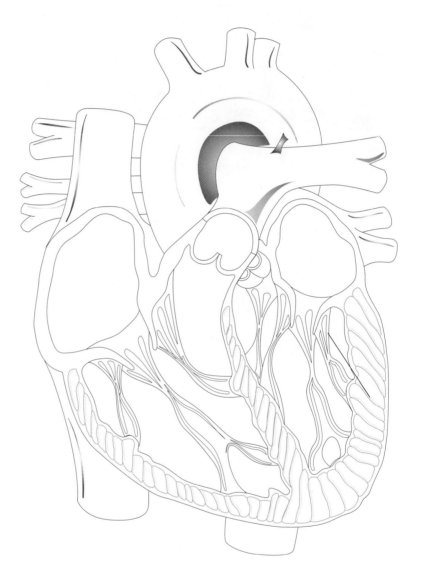

Additional Practice: The Cardiovascular System

Identify the location of each of the terms listed above the image. Write the name of the anatomical part on the corresponding line beneath the image.

1. Heart & Great Vessels I

right brachiocephalic vein   brachiocephalic artery   superior vena cava
pulmonary trunk   aorta   right ventricle
left ventricle   right atrium

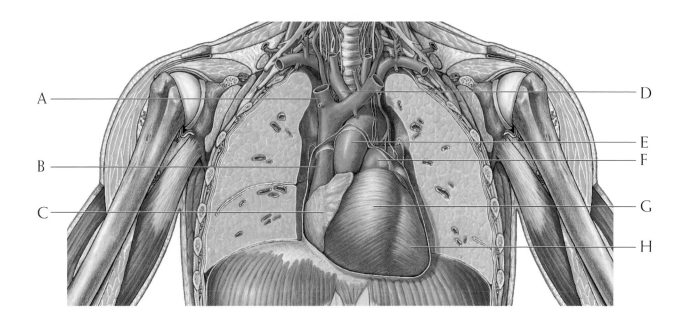

A. _____   E. _____

B. _____   F. _____

C. _____   G. _____

D. _____   H. _____

2. Heart & Great Vessels II

left common carotid artery   brachiocephalic trunk   left subclavian artery
left brachiocephalic vein   left pulmonary artery   inferior vena cava
right pulmonary artery   right pulmonary vein

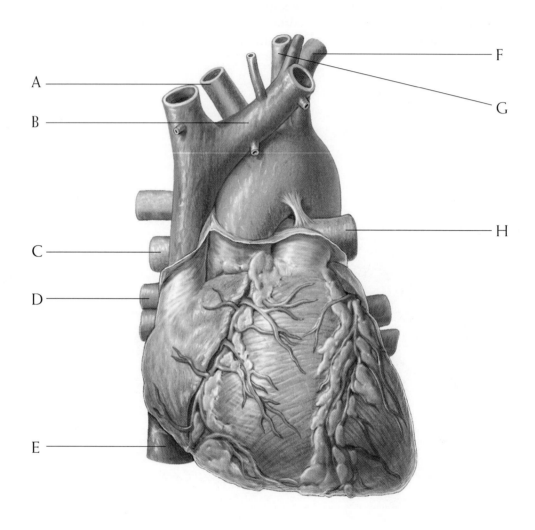

A. _____   E. _____

B. _____   F. _____

C. _____   G. _____

D. _____   H. _____

3. Heart & Great Vessels (Post)

left pulmonary artery   left subclavian artery   right brachiocephalic vein
left common carotid artery   right pulmonary artery   right pulmonary vein
left pulmonary vein   inferior vena cava

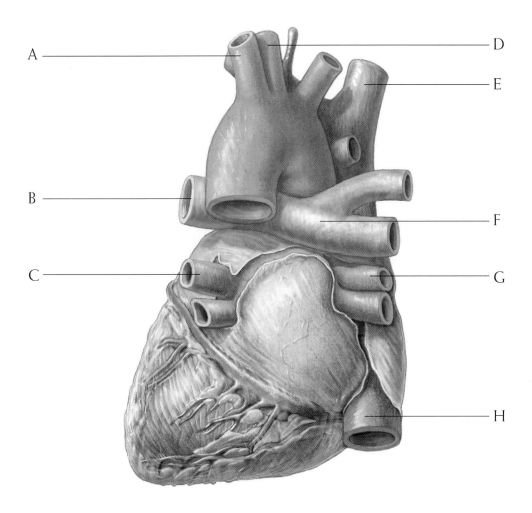

A. _____   E. _____

B. _____   F. _____

C. _____   G. _____

D. _____   H. _____

4. Arteries of Head & Neck

occipital artery   superficial temporal artery   external carotid artery
internal carotid artery   facial artery   vertebral artery
common carotid artery

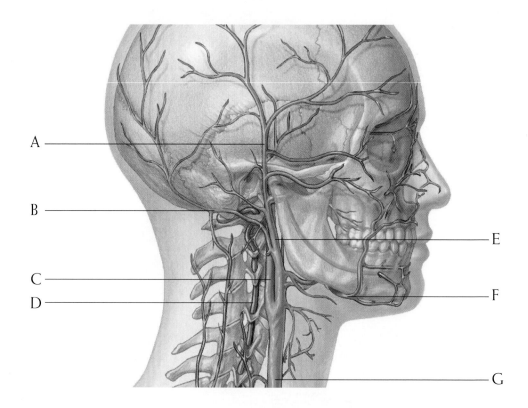

A. _____   E. _____

B. _____   F. _____

C. _____   G. _____

D. _____

5. Arteries of Trunk I

axillary artery
left common carotid
   artery

brachiocephalic trunk
left subclavian artery
thoracic aorta

right common carotid
   artery
arch of aorta

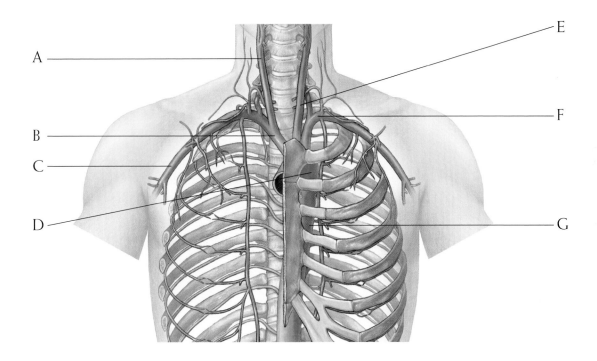

A. _____

B. _____

C. _____

D. _____

E. _____

F. _____

G. _____

6. Arteries of Trunk II

femoral artery   left common iliac artery   superior mesenteric artery
celiac trunk   inferior mesenteric artery   right renal artery
internal iliac artery   left renal artery

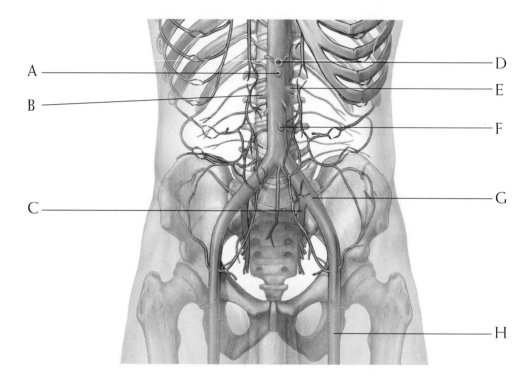

A. _____   E. _____

B. _____   F. _____

C. _____   G. _____

D. _____   H. _____

7. Arteries of Upper Limb

ulnar artery   subclavian artery   superficial palmar arterial arch
radial artery   brachial artery   axillary artery

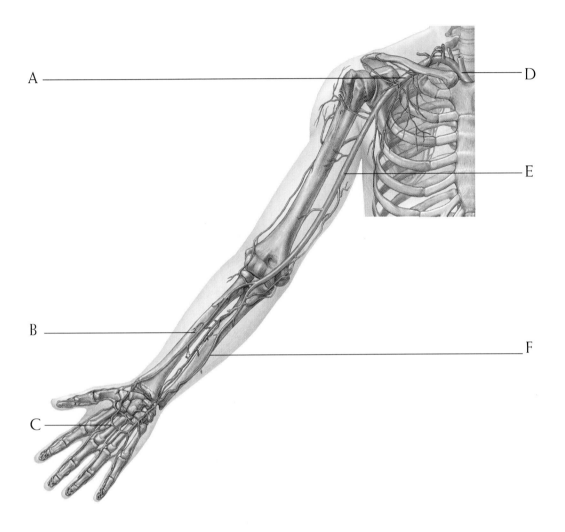

A. _____   D. _____

B. _____   E. _____

C. _____   F. _____

8. Arteries of Lower Limb (Post)

lateral circumflex femoral artery
popliteal artery

deep femoral artery
femoral artery

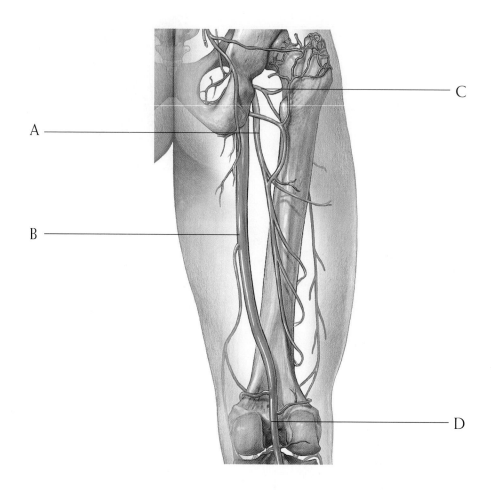

A. _____ C. _____

B. _____ D. _____

9. Veins of Head & Neck

external jugular vein   occipital vein   facial vein
internal jugular vein   brachiocephalic vein   subclavian vein

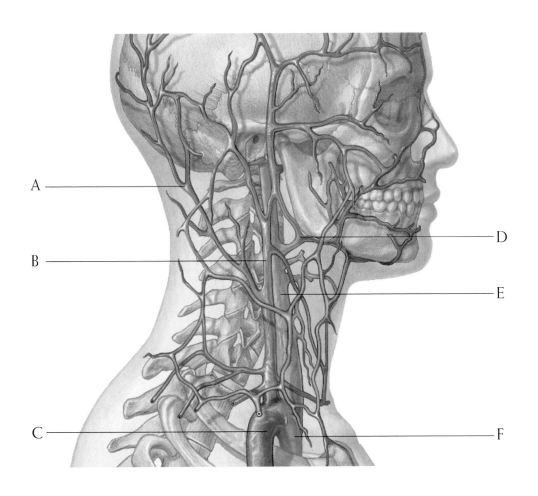

A. _____   D. _____

B. _____   E. _____

C. _____   F. _____

10. Veins of Trunk I

superior vena cava   axillary vein   subclavian vein
external jugular vein   internal jugular vein   right brachiocephalic vein
left brachiocephailic vein

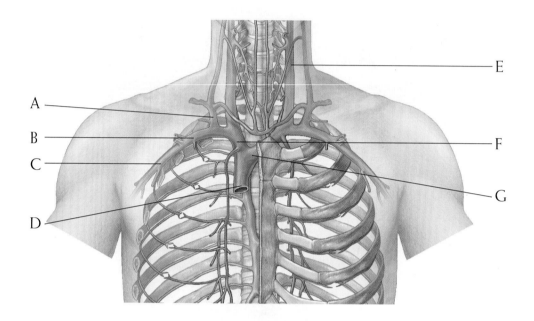

A. _____   E. _____

B. _____   F. _____

C. _____   G. _____

D. _____

11. Veins of Trunk II

femoral vein   great saphenous vein   right external iliac vein
right internal iliac vein   right common iliac vein   inferior vena cava
left common iliac vein   left external iliac vein

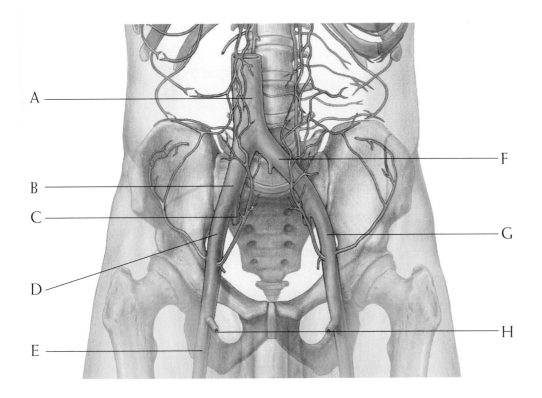

A. _____   E. _____

B. _____   F. _____

C. _____   G. _____

D. _____   H. _____

12. Veins of Upper Limb

ulnar vein   superficial palmar venous arch   basilic vein
radial vein   brachial vein   internal jugular vein
axillary vein

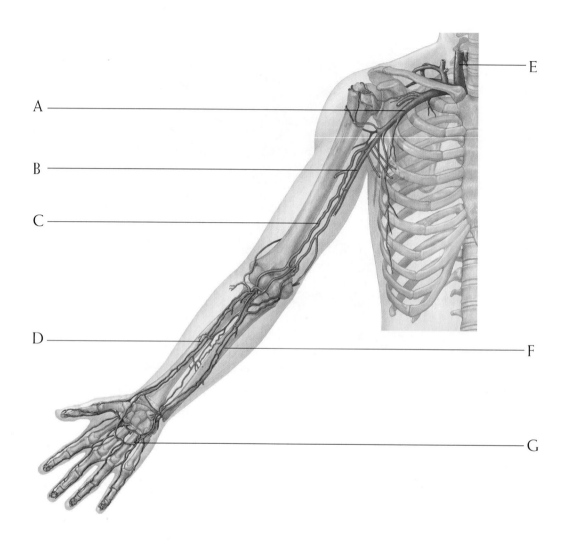

A. _____   E. _____

B. _____   F. _____

C. _____   G. _____

D. _____

13. Veins of Lower Limb (Post)

femoral vein   lateral circumflex femoral vein
popliteal vein   deep femoral vein

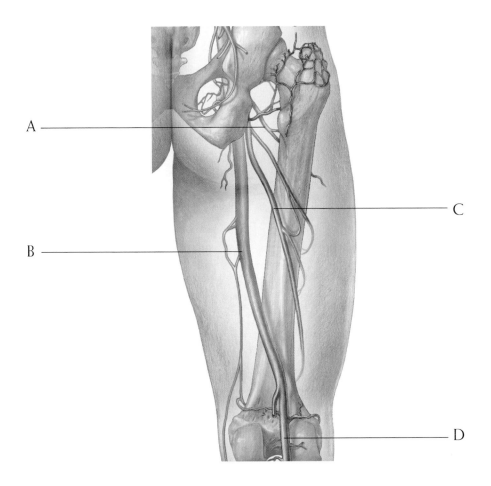

A. _____   C. _____

B. _____   D. _____

14. Hepatic Portal Veins

superior mesenteric vein   hepatic portal vein   inferior vena cava
splenic vein   inferior mesenteric vein   superior mesenteric vein
inferior vena cava

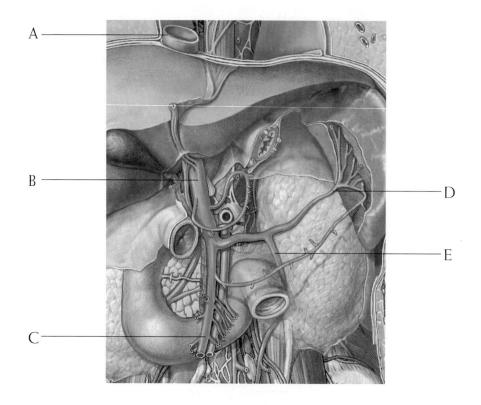

A. _____   D. _____

B. _____   E. _____

C. _____

15. Chambers of the Heart

right atrium   left atrium   left ventricle   right ventricle

The _____ receives oxygenated blood from the lungs.

The _____ receives deoxygenated blood from the body systems.

The _____ ejects deoxygenated blood to the lungs.

The _____ ejects oxygenated blood into the aorta.

Practical Application

Write brief responses to the following scenarios.

1. The heart is often described as a "dual pump." Give an explanation for this description. Include in your answer the oxygen and carbon dioxide gas levels of blood.

2. Explain why a person might feel more tired after standing still for a long period of time than if he or she had been walking at a leisurely pace for the same amount of time.

3. Plasma and interstitial fluid have essentially the same composition under normal body homeostasis, but interstitial fluid contains very little protein. Why?

4. The water component of plasma leaves the blood stream and enters tissue by the process of filtration. It is later reabsorbed by osmosis. Where does each of these processes for water movement between the blood and interstitial space occur? Why does water exit by filtration but reenter by osmosis? What is the significance of the protein imbalance between plasma and interstitial fluid in relation to water movement?

5. Assuming that the total length of the arteries in the body is approximately the same as the total length of the veins, which type of vessel contains more blood? Explain.

6. Use your knowledge of the cardiovascular system to explain why the skin turns red during periods of physical exertion.

7. A bacterial infection in the body can weaken the chordae tendinae and create a heart murmur. What is the name of a disease with this pathology, and what is the anatomical and mechanical connection between the weakened chordae tendinae and the resulting heart murmur?

8. Why does blood in the right side of the fetal heart mix with blood on the left side? Explain why this poses no problem for a fetus but would create a dangerous situation for a newborn baby.

9. An abnormal delay in the electrical conduction from the AV node to the bundle of His would affect which phase of the cardiac cycle? At what point of the ECG wave pattern would this be detectable?

10. The constriction of the arteries associated with hypertension creates an increased resistance to the ejection of the blood into the aorta following ventricular contraction. This means that less blood is able to exit the ventricle. How would this affect cardiac output, and how might the body compensate to maintain normal cardiac output?

Click on the Encyclopedia tab to open the A.D.A.M. Multimedia Encyclopedia in A.D.A.M. Interactive Anatomy. A quick search of key terms from the textbook will help you reinforce the knowledge you have gained thus far. Try entering pathological terms such as *endocarditis, angina pectoris, aneurysm, fibrillation, murmur,* or *tamponade* in the search bar to read more about these important topics related to the cardiovascular system.

Laboratory Activity 1

Identifying Heart Sounds

Background

Physicians listen to heart sounds because they serve as an indicator of cardiovascular disorders. A trained physician can detect slight variations in the sounds of blood flowing through the heart that may indicate abnormalities in the atria, ventricles, and/or valves. Physicians can correlate heart sounds with the waves of an ECG to get a full picture of a person's cardiac health. This activity will allow you to practice listening to both abnormal and normal heart sounds.

Materials

- Lab partner
- Alcohol swabs
- Stethoscope
- Stopwatch or clock with second hand
- Internet access

Procedure

1. Wipe the ear pieces of the stethoscope with an alcohol swab. Let the alcohol dry and then place the ear pieces in your ears.
2. Have your lab partner place the bell of the stethoscope on his or her chest, just over the heart.
3. Listen for the heart sounds, and ask your lab partner to move the bell around until you hear them clearly. Notice the two-beat rhythm of the heart (a "lubb-dupp" sound).

4. Identify the first sound. It is the sound of atrial contraction being completed as the valves close. Ventricular contraction begins at this point.
5. Next, listen for the second sound. It marks the end of ventricular contraction as the valves leading to the aorta and pulmonary arteries close.
6. Use the stopwatch or timer to measure the time interval between the first and second sounds.
7. Time the interval between the second sound and the next first sound. After five of these intervals, calculate the average time the heart is at rest in 1 minute, and the average time the heart is in contraction in 1 minute.
8. Switch roles with your lab partner and repeat steps 3 through 10.
9. Go to http://anatphys.emcp.net/HeartSound or search online for audio featuring a normal heart sound. Listen to the recording.
10. Determine whether the sounds you heard and measured from your lab partner match the normal heart sounds from the recording.
11. Next, try to identify how the sounds of the abnormal heart differ from those of the normal heart.

Analysis

Write a one- to two-paragraph evaluation of your findings.

Laboratory Activity 2

Identifying Venous Valves

Background

Venous valves ensure that the blood returning to the heart does not flow back to the various parts of the body. Certain venous disorders prevent the valves from doing their job. This can cause a variety of problems ranging from impaired blood flow to a buildup of fluids in organs and limbs. This activity will guide you through a simple test used to investigate the integrity of the venous system.

Procedure

1. If you are wearing a long-sleeve shirt, roll up the sleeve of one arm to expose the veins on the forearm.
2. Hold your arm with your hand facing down, and clench your fist several times so that the veins appear larger.
3. Place the forefinger of your other hand on one of the larger veins, and push your thumb along the vein toward your shoulder. Observe whether part of the vein "disappears" as the blood is milked out of it.
4. Remove your thumb, leaving your forefinger in place on the vein. Observe whether the blood flows back into the vein. (Blood should not flow back if the valve is working properly.)
5. Remove your forefinger and observe what happens.
6. Place your finger back on the vein, and push your thumb along the vein, moving toward your hand. Leave your finger in place, release your thumb, and observe whether the blood flows back into the vein. Remove your finger, and observe what happens.

7. Based on your observations, predict where the valves are located in the vein.

Analysis

Write a brief analysis explaining your observations and what they might indicate. Hypothesize how body position, altitude, and gravity affect the function of venous valves.

1. Which of the following is *false* regarding pulse and blood pressure?
   a) Pulse is detectable because of blood pressure.
   b) An increase in pulse always indicates an increase in blood pressure.
   c) Pulse is an indication of heart rate.
   d) Blood pressure is a measure of the force of the blood on the blood vessels.

2. Which of the following types of blood vessels carry blood that has a high oxygen content?
   a) all arteries
   b) all veins
   c) pulmonary arteries
   d) systemic arteries

3. What effect would dehydration have on the hydrostatic pressure of blood?
   a) It would cause it to increase.
   b) It would cause it to decrease.
   c) It would cause it to fluctuate rapidly.
   d) It would have no effect.

4. Which of the three layers found in blood vessels differs the most between arteries and veins?
   a) the tunica media
   b) the tunica intima
   c) the tunica adventitia
   d) All differ equally.

5. Contraction of arterial muscles:
   a) occurs in the tunica media
   b) is called vasoconstriction
   c) narrows the lumen
   d) All of the above

6. Exchange of material between the blood and the body occurs in the:
   a) capillaries
   b) arterioles
   c) veins
   d) All of the above

7. Fenestrated capillaries would be *least* likely to be found in the:
   a) brain
   b) kidneys
   c) small intestines
   d) pituitary gland

8. Which of the following is true about the atria of the heart?
   a) They receive blood.
   b) They exchange blood with one another.
   c) They contain blood that is high in oxygen.
   d) All of the above

9. Which of the following is true about the ventricles of the heart?
   a) They are completely emptied during systole.
   b) They fill with blood during diastole.
   c) They contain blood that is high in oxygen.
   d) All of the above

10. Pericardial fluid is contained within which of the following membrane layers surrounding the heart?
    a) the myocardium and the epicardium
    b) the serous pericardium and the fibrous pericardium
    c) the fibrous pericardium and the epicardium
    d) All of the above

11. Coronary blood vessels:
    a) supply the myocardium with blood
    b) consist of arteries that are high in oxygen and veins that are low in oxygen
    c) can cause cardiac infarction if blocked
    d) All of the above

12. Which of the following is *false* about the AV valves?
    a) They operate through direct sympathetic enervation.
    b) They prevent backflow of blood into the atria.
    c) The left is called the bicuspid and the right is called the tricuspid.
    d) Their abnormal stretching is called prolapse.

13. Semilunar valves:
    a) prevent backflow of blood into the ventricles
    b) are forced open as a result of ventricular contraction
    c) are also called the aortic and pulmonary valves
    d) All of the above

14. The right side of the heart:
    a) sends blood into pulmonary circulation
    b) contains blood high in oxygen
    c) contracts with more force than the left side
    d) All of the above

15. An artificial pacemaker replaces the function of which of the following collections of cardiac muscle cells?
    a) the bundle of His
    b) the Purkinje fibers
    c) the SA node
    d) AV node

16. An average normal resting heart rate is:
    a) 50 bpm
    b) 75 bpm
    c) 90 bpm
    d) 120 bpm

17. Which of the following sequences is the correct pathway of electrical conduction in the heart?
    a) AV node, SA node, bundle of His, Purkinje system
    b) SA node, AV node, Purkinje system, bundle of His
    c) SA node, AV node, bundle of His, Purkinje system
    d) Sa node, bundle of His, AV node, Purkinje system

18. The ductus arteriosus:
    a) provides the fetal lungs with oxygen
    b) separates the right and left atria of the fetal heart
    c) provides a way for blood to bypass the fetal lungs
    d) All of the above

19. The QRS complex of an ECG:
    a) represents ventricular depolarization and contraction
    b) would be widened by a delay in electrical conduction by the bundle of His
    c) corresponds with ventricular systole
    d) All of the above

20. The distance from the beginning of one P wave to the beginning of the next P wave:
    a) is called the P-R interval
    b) corresponds to one complete contraction and relaxation of the heart
    c) decreases with a slowing heartbeat
    d) can be used to measure blood pressure

21. Diastole occurs as a result of:
    a) atrial depolarization
    b) ventricular filling
    c) atrial contraction
    d) ventricular relaxation

22. Which of the following describes an aspect of congestive heart failure?
    a) More than the normal amount of blood remains in the ventricles following systole.
    b) Body tissues do not receive adequate oxygen.
    c) Blood enters the heart faster than it can be pumped out.
    d) All of the above

23. Fibrillation is an example of:
    a) thrombosis
    b) arrhythmia
    c) hypertrophy
    d) aneurysm

24. A heart valve prolapse is associated with:
    a) blood regurgitation
    b) heart murmur
    c) reduced blood-pumping capacity
    d) All of the above

25. Which of the following is *not* a normal effect of aging on the cardiovascular system?
    a) arterial stiffness
    b) increased maximal heart rate
    c) varicose veins
    d) decreased cardiovagal baroreflex

CHAPTER

THE LYMPHATIC SYSTEM
AND THE BLOOD

Introduction

The lymphatic system helps the body fight infection. It is composed of several organs and vessels that carry lymphocytes throughout the body. The lymphatic system also helps to maintain fluid balance in tissues. The blood is composed of a variety of cells (red blood cells, white blood cells, and platelets) contained in a fluid matrix called plasma. Red blood cells transport respiratory gases, platelets are responsible for blood clotting, and white blood cells serve to protect the body from infection and abnormal cell growth (cancer). The following exercises will require you to apply what you have learned about the blood and the lymphatic system. Refer to Chapter 12 of *Applied Anatomy & Physiology, A Case Study Approach* for assistance, if necessary. Access A.D.A.M. Interactive Anatomy for additional information that will provide an opportunity to deepen your understanding of the concepts presented in the textbook.

Completion

Complete the following sentences by filling in each blank with a key term from the text.

1. Blood is composed of a fluid matrix called _____ and three types of cellular components: red blood cells, or _____; white blood cells, or _____; and _____, also known as _____.

2. The _____ system makes and transports _____ to fight infection.

3. There are three types of white blood cells known as _____: _____, _____, and _____; and there are two types of white blood cells known as _____: _____ and _____.

4. Blood cells, which are derived from _____, or _____, stem cells, develop into either a white-blood-cell producer, called a(n) _____ _____; or a red blood cell, platelet, and circulating white-blood-cell producer called a(n) _____ _____.

5. The structural components of the lymphatic system include the lymphatic _____, _____ _____, _____, _____, and _____ blood cells.

6. The immune system responds to disease using two mechanisms: _____ immunity, which is _____ and includes barriers to infection, and _____ immunity, which is very specific and responds in two stages: the _____ _____, which is the initial response to an antigen, and the _____ response, which occurs upon a subsequent exposure to the same antigen.

7. When macrophages attach to ___ lymphocytes they produce _____ _____ that make antibodies or _____, as well as _____ _____ that store the information to produce antibodies.

8. The immunity that results from antibody production by B lymphocytes is called _____ _____, while immunity resulting from intact cells—primarily T lymphocytes—is called _____-_____ _____.

9. Immunity against disease can be acquired through _____ immunity, which is gained by exposure to foreign antigens, or through _____ immunity, which requires the introduction of antibodies.

10. Various types of _____ result from deficiency of red blood cells. Insufficient vitamin B12 causes _____ _____; a genetic disorder called _____-_____ _____ causes a type of _____, or abnormal hemoglobin disorder; and the presence of abnormally large or abnormally small red blood cells causes _____ and _____ _____, respectively.

Matching

Match each of the following terms with the corresponding description by writing the letter of the term on the blank next to the correct description.

a) antigens

b) basophils

c) B lymphocytes

d) circulating monocytes

e) eosinophils

f) erythropoiesis

g) fibrin

h) hematocrit

i) mast cell

j) megakaryocytes

k) MCHC

l) plasmin

m) prostacyclin

n) red pulp

o) Rh factor

_____ prevents platelet activation

_____ area of the spleen that stores and removes RBCs

_____ packed red cell volume

_____ induce immune response

_____ bone marrow platelet producer

_____ dissolves blood clots

_____ average RBC hemoglobin concentration

_____ produce antibodies

_____ WBCs that secrete histamine

_____ protein necessary for blood clot formation

_____ type-D RBC protein

_____ phagocytic blood cells

_____ secretions contain major basic protein

_____ associated with inflammation

_____ red blood cell formation

Complete the Terms Table

Fill in the missing key terms and/or definitions in the following table.

Term	Definition
	a protein in red blood cells that carries oxygen
reticulocyte	
mean corpuscular volume (MCV)	
	the mass of hemoglobin molecules in each red blood cell
	a classification system for the proteins on human red blood cells
carbonic anhydrase	
	an enzyme that stimulates blood clotting by converting fibrinogen into fibrin
Peyer's patches	
	a region of the spleen composed of lymphatic tissue
	a group of innate immunity plasma proteins that can be activated to destroy microorganisms
antibody	
	a T-lymphocyte that inhibits the immune response
	therapeutic exposure to foreign antigens
hemophilia	
	a condition in which the body produces an immune response against its own organs or tissues

Label the Graphic

Identify each of the following terms in the illustration on the next page. Write the number of the corresponding blood cell on the line indicating its location. Then answer the questions that follow.

1. B lymphocyte
2. basophil
3. eosinophil
4. lymphoid stem cell
5. macrophage
6. megakaryocyte
7. monocyte
8. myeloid stem cell
9. neutrophil
10. plasma cell
11. platelets
12. pre-B cell
13. pre-T cell
14. red blood cell
15. reticulocyte
16. T lymphocyte
17. tissue mast cell

multipotent stem cell

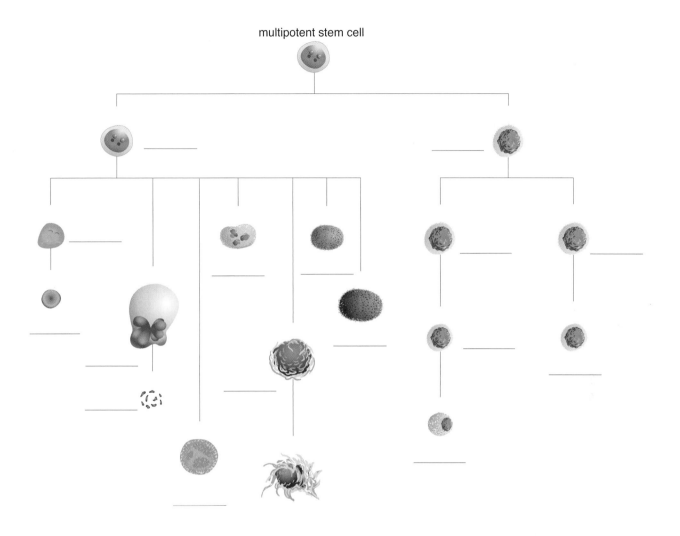

1. Which of the final cells produced are called granulocytes?

2. Which of the final cells produced are called agranulocytes?

3. Which of the final components of blood lack nuclei?

Color the Graphic

Color this illustration using the following color key. Then answer the questions that accompany it.

axillary lymph nodes – dark blue
cervical lymph nodes – green
inguinal lymph nodes – yellow
lymph vessels of the lumbar trunk – highlight in yellow
popliteal lymph nodes – black
spleen – red
submandibular lymph nodes – brown
thoracic duct – highlight in pink
thymus – light blue
tonsils – orange

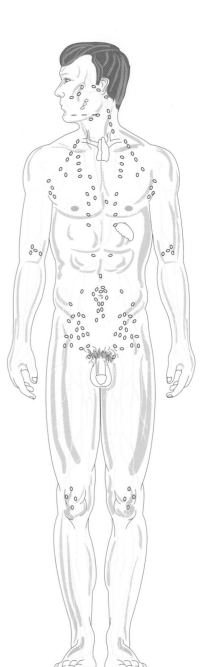

1. What are the four components of lymph nodes?

2. What is the name of the location of a lymph node where the blood vessels enter and exit?

3. What is the name of the fluid-filled sac within a lymph node?

4. What is the name of the capsular wall partitions within a lymph node that create regions housing B- and T-cell lymphocytes?

A.D.A.M. Education

For additional information on common conditions associated with the cardiovascular and lymphatic systems, click on the Clinical Illustrations tab and narrow your search by choosing either *Lymphatic* or *Immune* from the Body System menu. A quick search of each topic will lead you to a variety of images to explore including: *swollen lymph nodes, lower leg edema, splenomegaly, blood cells, allergies, immunizations, antibody formation,* and *HIV*.

Additional Practice: The Lymphatic System

Identify the location of each of the terms listed above the image. Write the name of the anatomical part on the corresponding line beneath the image.

A.D.A.M. Education

For additional assistance on the labeling exercises, open A.D.A.M. Interactive Anatomy and click on the Atlas Anatomy tab. Next, refine your search by selecting either *Immune* or *Lymphatic* from the Body System menu and *Illustration* from the Image Type menu. To find examples of organs or tissues that contribute to more than one body system (i.e. lymphocytes, which contribute to both blood and lymph), enter the desired name in the search bar at the top of the screen and match the presented options to the images in this section.

1. Cervical Nodes

deep parotid lymph node   submandibular lymph node
occipital lymph node   deep cervical lymph node

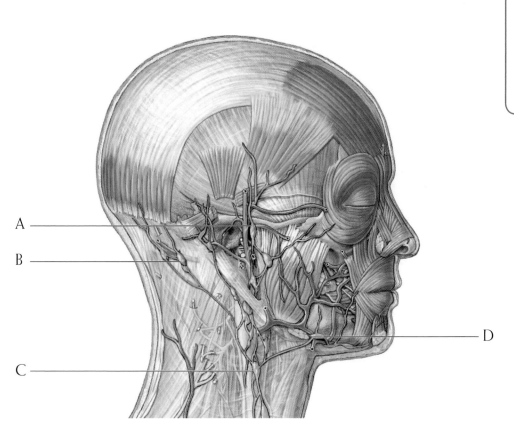

A. _____   C. _____
B. _____   D. _____

2. Cysterna Chyli

thoracic duct

lumbar lymph node

intercostal lymph node

cysterna chyli

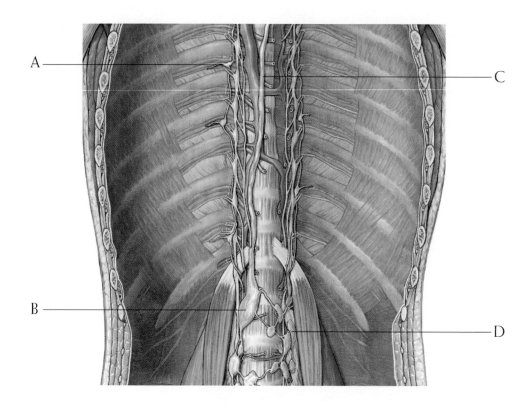

A. _____   C. _____

B. _____   D. _____

3. Spleen

spleen   splenic vein   splenic artery
pancreas   gallbladder   portal vein

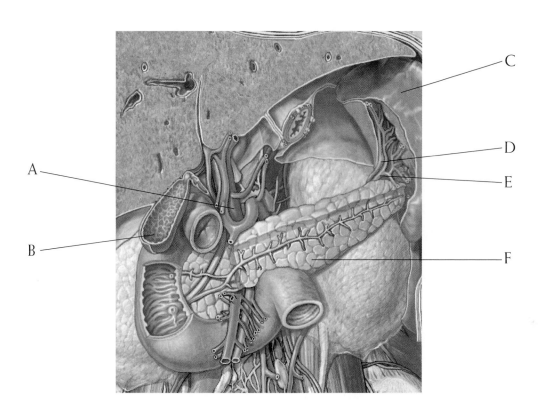

A. _____   D. _____

B. _____   E. _____

C. _____   F. _____

You may need to reference the respiratory system chapter (Chapter 10) to complete this exercise.

4. Thymus

epiglottis	thoracic duct	left brachiocephalic vein
thymus gland	trachea	cricoid cartilage
thyroid cartilage	hyoid bone	

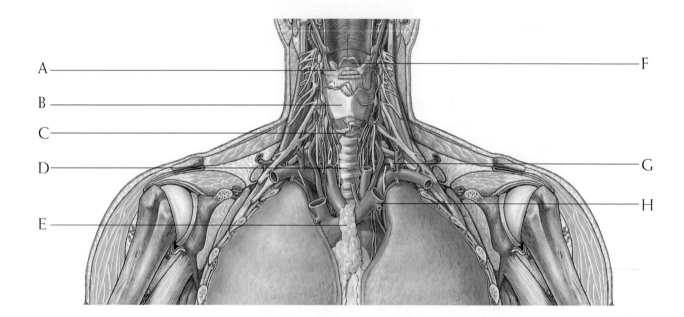

A. _____ E. _____

B. _____ F. _____

C. _____ G. _____

D. _____ H. _____

5. Tonsils I

pharyngeal tonsil (adenoids) nasopharynx oropharynx
internal jugular vein palatine tonsil lingual tonsil

You may need to reference the respiratory system chapter (Chapter 10) to complete this exercise.

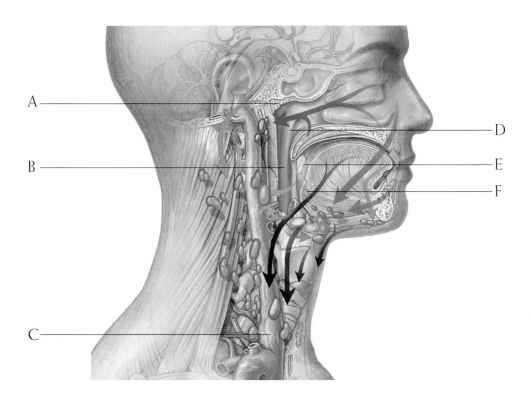

A. _____   D. _____

B. _____   E. _____

C. _____   F. _____

6. Tonsils II

palatine   tubal   pharyngeal   lingual

The _____ tonsils are found at the back of the throat.

The _____ tonsils are found in the nasopharynx.

The _____ tonsils are found at the base of the tongue.

The _____ tonsils surround the openings of the auditory tubes into the pharynx.

7. Lymphatic Glands

lymph nodes   tonsils   thymus   spleen

The _____ filter lymph and house lymphocytes to fight infection.

The _____ is active in childhood but becomes less functional as we age.

The _____ is responsible for filtering blood rather than lymph and also aids in the

recycling of red blood cells.

The _____ are found within the nasal and oral respiratory passageways to filter pathogens that may be breathed in through the air.

8. Cells

B-lymphocyte   Memory   T-lymphocyte   Plasma

_____ cells are responsible for "Humoral" immunity.

_____ cells are responsible for "Cell-mediated" immunity.

_____ cells are responsible for the majority of antibody production.

_____ cells can recognize a pathogen that the body has seen in the past.

9. Immunity

Active natural   Active artificial   Passive natural   Passive artificial

_____ immunity results from coming in contact with a pathogen and contracting a disease.

_____ immunity results from receiving a vaccination.

_____ immunity results from mom passing antibodies to the child via the placenta and breast milk.

_____ immunity results from receiving an injection of serum containing antibodies made by another individual or animal.

Practical Application

Write brief responses to the following scenarios.

1. Is it always a good idea to immediately treat a mild fever with fever-reducing medication? Why or why not?

2. What effect would dehydration of the body have on a hematocrit reading and why?

3. Would it be possible for an individual to have had a malignancy at some point in his or her lifetime that he or she never knew about and that no longer exists? Explain.

4. The lower oxygen content of air at high elevations causes an increase in red blood cell production. How would this affect blood viscosity, and what problem might this pose for an individual with hypertension?

5. Describe the importance of the vasodilatory effect of histamine during the immune response.

6. When bilirubin accumulates in the blood plasma, it causes the skin and whites of the eyes to appear yellow in color—a condition known as *jaundice*. Bilirubin is normally removed from the body by the liver and digestive system. Assuming that the liver and digestive system are functioning properly, what blood abnormality might jaundice indicate?

7. What pathological condition is indicated when cells produce interferons?

8. Compare and contrast the immune system's role in the spleen and lymph nodes.

9. A dangerous practice used by some athletes called "blood doping" involves injecting commercially prepared erythropoietin into the body prior to an athletic competition. What benefit are these athletes seeking, and what is dangerous about this practice?

10. The blood of a mother does not normally "mix" with the blood of a fetus, but it is possible for some of the fetal blood to leak into the mother's blood in the late stages of pregnancy and/or during birth. What risk would this pose in a situation where the mother is Rh negative but the child is Rh positive? To whom does the risk factor belong? Could this affect subsequent pregnancies? (Note that while fetal and maternal blood do not normally mix, antibodies are small enough to diffuse through the maternal and fetal circulatory membranes.)

Laboratory Activity 1

Pathology of the Blood and Lymphatic System

Background

A biopsy and microscopic analysis of blood, lymph nodes, and red bone marrow is sometimes necessary to identify cancers and blood-related diseases. A biopsy is the removal and analysis of live tissues from a patient. Pathologists compare normal images of the tissue to the samples from the patient. This helps them to determine any visible differences that may indicate an abnormality. However, before they can do this, they must practice comparing the normal samples to pictures to help them determine the different components and cell types that make up the blood and lymphatic system.

Materials

- Microscope with high-power capability (400X)
- Prepared slide of normal red bone marrow
- Prepared slide of normal human blood
- Internet access

Procedure and Analysis

Place the slide of the red bone marrow under the microscope. Start with low magnification and move to higher magnification to see details and individual cells. Go to http://anatphys.emcp.net/Hematopathology and compare what you see under the microscope with the images listed below. Can you find the RBC precursors (erythroid precursors) and WBC precursors (granulocytic precursors) in the bone marrow you are studying?

- Normal bone marrow, medium-power microscopic image
- Normal bone marrow, high-power microscopic image
- Normal bone marrow smear, high-power microscopic image No. 3
- Normal bone marrow smear, high-power microscopic image No. 4
- Normal bone marrow smear, high-power microscopic image No. 5

Place the blood slide under the microscope and compare it with the images listed below. Can you identify the RBCs and the different types of WBCs?

- Normal RBCs on the smear, microscopic image
- WBC identification, microscopic image

Now, view the images of the following diseased specimens on the same website:

- Hypochromic microcytic anemia on smear, microscopic
- CBC with iron deficiency anemia, diagram
- Hypersegmented neutrophil with megaloblastic anemia on smear, microscopic image
- CBC with megaloblastic anemia, diagram
- Atypical lymphocytes on smear, microscopic image
- Sickle cell disease on smear, microscopic image
- Acute myeloblastic leukemia on smear, microscopic image

continued

- Acute myeloblastic leukemia in bone marrow, low power microscopic image

Can you recognize the differences in the types of cells that characterize each disease? Write a brief analysis summarizing your findings in this activity.

Laboratory Activity 2

Assessing Potential Allergens

Background

The Environmental Protection Agency (EPA) recognizes that indoor air quality (IAQ) is the cause of many illnesses at home, school, and work. It is estimated that Americans spend up to 90% of their time indoors, and the EPA estimates that poor IAQ costs billions of dollars a year in medical care and missed work. A variety of pollutants can reduce the quality of the air in a building. Microorganisms such as bacteria and mold contribute to allergies and respiratory diseases. Cockroach parts, dust mites, fur, and pollen are indoor contaminants that aggravate allergies and asthma. Skin cells carry viruses that can cause respiratory diseases. This activity investigates a simple way to detect the presence of potential allergens and other substances that reduce IAQ.

Materials

- Clear tape
- Small centimeter ruler
- Three nutrient agar Petri plates per test
- Incubator set at 37°C
- Microscope with high-power capability (400X)
- Five clean microscope slides per sampling
- Internet access

Procedure and Analysis: Microorganism Collection

1. Collect three nutrient agar Petri plates and leave them uncovered in three different areas of the room. Try to select areas that differ in air flow, elevation, level of foot traffic , and/or proximity to doors.
2. Let the plates remain open for 30 minutes.
3. After 30 minutes, put the lids on the Petri plates and place them in a warm area of the room or in an incubator set at 37°C for 2 days.
4. After the 2-day period, remove the Petri plates from the incubator and carefully view the types of microorganisms growing on the agar surface of each Petri plate. Do not remove the lids.
5. Identify your specimens by conducting an Internet search to find images of bacteria and fungi growing on Petri plates. Use the terms "bacteria culture" and "mold culture" to conduct two separate searches.
6. See if you can tell whether bacteria and mold are growing on your Petri plates. Do the Petri plates that were placed in different locations differ in the types of growth?
7. Compare your Petri plates with those of other students.

Procedure and Analysis: Dust Collection

1. Prepare five 2-cm pieces of tape
2. Place the sticky side of each piece of tape on a different surface. You might try tabletops, clothing, shoe bottoms, and air vents.
3. Stick each piece of tape to the center of a different microscope slide.
4. Place one slide under the microscope lens. Start with low magnification and move to higher magnification to see details of the dust particles.
5. Look up photographs of the various dust particles by conducting a Google Image search (http://anatphys.emcp.net/GoogleImages) using terms such as "cockroach," "cat hair," "dog hair," "dust mites," and "dust particles" to find appropriate images. Also search for the term "forensic fibers" for more photographs of materials found in dirt and dust.
6. Repeat steps 4 and 5 for each slide.
7. See what types of potential allergens you can find on the different materials you sampled.
8. Compare what you found with other students' samples.

Quiz

1. Which of the following distinguishes blood from other types of connective tissue?
   a) It supports other body tissues.
   b) It contains cells and a matrix.
   c) It has a fluid matrix.
   d) Its cells are in a dispersed arrangement.

2. Which of the following would *not* be considered "complete" cells?
   a) erythrocytes
   b) thrombocytes
   c) platelets
   d) All of the above

3. Which of the following values of a CBC would be expressed as a percentage?
   a) hematocrit
   b) MCV
   c) MCH
   d) All of the above

4. A person with type O blood:
   a) could be a recipient of all other blood types
   b) could be a donor for all other blood types
   c) has a protein called type O on their red blood cells
   d) All of the above

5. Erythroblastosis fetalis occurs when:
   a) a mother and her developing fetus have incompatible ABO blood types
   b) either the mother or the developing fetus is Rh positive and the other is Rh negative
   c) a mother is Rh negative and her developing fetus is Rh positive
   d) All of the above

6. In a normal differential white blood cell count, the highest percentage of cells would be:
   a) neutrophils
   b) erythrocytes
   c) lymphocytes
   d) eosinophils

7. A patient with a parasitic infection would probably have an abnormally high count of:
   a) erythrocytes
   b) monocytes
   c) neutrophils
   d) eosinophils

8. Which of the following is *not* a granulocyte?
   a) eosinophil
   b) basophil
   c) lymphocyte
   d) neutrophil

9. How many molecules of oxygen would be carried per cubic millimeter of blood in a person with a normal red blood cell count?
   a) 4 million
   b) 20 million
   c) 120,000
   d) 1 billion

10. Which of the following is *not* a function of red blood cells?
    a) to transport oxygen to tissue
    b) to transport carbon dioxide to the lungs
    c) to stimulate bicarbonate-ion formation
    d) to aid in the immune response

11. Monocytes in tissue are phagocytic cells called:
    a) mast cells
    b) macrophages
    c) basic protein cells
    d) microglia

12. Which of the following represents a correct sequence in clot formation and destruction?
    a) platelet adhesion, fibrinogen, fibrin, plasminogen, plasmin
    b) plasminogen, plasmin, platelet adhesion, prothrombin, thrombin
    c) prothrombin, thrombin, plasminogen, plasmin, clot dissolving
    d) platelet adhesion, prothrombin, thrombin, fibrinogen, fibrin

13. What type of cell is *not* produced by bone-marrow myeloid progenitor cells?
    a) platelet
    b) lymphocyte
    c) macrophage
    d) erythrocyte

14. Which of the following is *not* a component of the lymphatic system?
    a) the thyroid
    b) the thymus
    c) the spleen
    d) leukocytes

15. The removal of red blood cells is accomplished by:
    a) the thymus
    b) the white pulp of the spleen
    c) the red pulp of the spleen
    d) All of the above

16. Which of the following is *not* an agent of innate immunity?
    a) skin
    b) complements
    c) natural killer cells
    d) helper T cells

17. The primary response of acquired immunity involves:
    a) macrophage phagocytosis of an antigen
    b) B lymphocytes dividing into plasma cells and memory cells
    c) antibody production by B lymphocytes
    d) All of the above

18. The elevation of this antibody could indicate an allergic reaction:
    a) IgM
    b) IgE
    c) IgD
    d) IgA

19. A vaccine that induces active immunity works by introducing
    _____ into the body.
    a) antibodies
    b) antibiotics
    c) antigens
    d) All of the above

20. Breast-feeding provides an infant with:
    a) antigens
    b) globulins
    c) antibodies
    d) All of the above

21. Which of the following is *not* a cause of anemia?
    a) high altitude
    b) iron deficiency
    c) internal bleeding
    d) kidney damage

22. A major symptom of lymph vessel blockage is:
    a) fever
    b) swelling
    c) paralysis
    d) anemia

23. HIV causes AIDS by attacking:
    a) B lymphocytes
    b) suppressor T cells
    c) helper T cells
    d) All of the above

24. Which of the following is *not* associated with hypersensitivity?
    a) IgE antibodies
    b) major basic protein
    c) mast cells
    d) histamine

25. Which of the following is associated with the reduced red blood cell production that accompanies aging?
    a) diminished nutrient absorption
    b) presence of fewer bone marrow stem cells
    c) decrease in kidney erythropoietin
    d) All of the above

The Digestive System

Introduction

The digestive system consists of the alimentary canal and the accessory organs that contribute secretions to aid in the digestive process. The digestive system makes it possible for the body to break down complex molecules of food into the simple molecules needed for energy and the raw materials necessary for building cellular components. These nutrients are then transported by the blood to all of the other organ systems, which depend on the digestive system to meet their nutritional needs. The following exercises and lab activities will require you to apply what you have learned about the digestive system. Refer to Chapter 13 of *Applied Anatomy & Physiology, A Case Study Approach* for assistance, if necessary. Access A.D.A.M. Interactive Anatomy for additional information and opportunities to deepen your understanding of the concepts presented in the textbook.

Completion

Complete the following sentences by filling in each blank with a key term from the text.

1. The digestive system is composed of two components: the _____ _____ or _____ _____ and the _____ _____ _____.

2. The accessory digestive organs include the _____ _____, _____, _____, and _____.

3. The four major types of teeth, beginning with the center position and moving laterally and posteriorly, are the _____, _____, _____, and _____.

4. The four layers of tissue that make up the esophagus and the rest of the alimentary canal, from deep to superficial, are the _____ _____, _____, _____, and _____.

5. The three regions of the stomach, from superior to inferior, are the _____, _____, and _____ regions.

6. The three sections of the small intestine, beginning with the section located proximal to the stomach, are the _____, _____, and _____.

7. The five regions of the large intestine, or _____, beginning proximal to the small intestines, are the _____, _____, _____, _____, and _____ portions.

8. Exocrine cell clusters of the pancreas called _____ produce inactive enzymes called _____ as well as active enzymes that are transported to the _____ by way of the _____ and _____ _____ ducts.

9. The three major hormones that control digestion are _____, _____, and _____.

10. A _____ _____ is a protrusion of the upper part of the stomach into the thorax, and a _____ _____ is a protrusion of the small intestine into the pelvic muscles.

Matching

Match each of the following terms with the corresponding description by writing the letter of the term on the blank next to the correct description.

a) buccal

b) cardiac sphincter

c) chief cells

d) chyme

e) diverticulosis

f) dysphagia

g) hepatocytes

h) ileocecal valve

i) palate

j) paneth cells

k) parotid

l) peristalsis

m) pyloric sphincter

n) sublingual

o) villi

_____ lower stomach sphincter muscle

_____ separates the small and large intestines

_____ associated with the cheeks

_____ moves food through digestive tract

_____ projections of the mucosa in the small intestine

_____ salivary gland anterior to the ear

_____ causes difficult or painful swallowing

_____ lower esophageal sphincter muscle

_____ salivary gland beneath the tongue

_____ partially digested food

_____ produce digestive enzymes in the stomach

_____ liver cells

_____ causes pockets to form in the large intestine

_____ roof of the mouth

_____ produce antibacterial enzymes

✿A.D.A.M. Education

To view an animated presentation of peristalsis, click on the Clinical Animations tab within A.D.A.M. Interactive Anatomy. Refine your search by choosing *Digestive* from the Body System menu, clicking the search button, and then choosing the animation titled *Peristalsis*.

Fill in the missing key terms and/or definitions in the following table.

Term	Definition
	a layer of connective tissue underneath the epithelium of mucosa
	secretory cells of the stomach that produce hydrochloric acid
microvilli	
mesentery	
	absorptive cells of the small intestine
ingestion	
	taken into the body but bypassing the digestive tract
salivary amylase	
enterokinase	
	condition due to a combination of esophageal and gastric reflux
	protistan infection that produces extreme abdominal cramping and chronic diarrhea
cirrhosis	
	excessive bacterial gas production in the large intestine
faliciform ligament	
	a region of the hypothalamus that signals a person has eaten

Label the Graphic

Identify each of the following terms in the illustrations on the next page. Write the number of the anatomical part in the box indicating its location. Then asnwer the questions that follow.

Figure 1 Terms

1. body
2. cardiac sphincter
3. circular muscle layer
4. duodenum
5. esophagus
6. fundus
7. gastroesophageal opening
8. longitudinal muscle layer
9. oblique muscle layer
10. pyloric sphincter
11. pylorus

Figure 2 Terms

1. aorta
2. ascending colon
3. cecum
4. descending colon
5. ileocecal valve
6. ileum
7. inferior vena cava
8. rectum
9. sigmoid colon
10. transverse colon
11. vermiform appendix

Figure 1 The Stomach

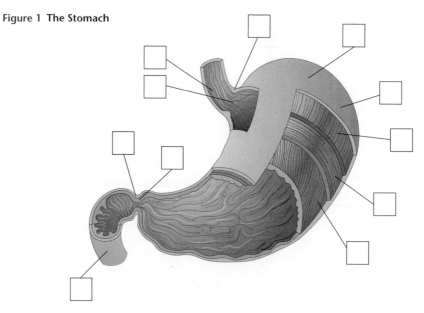

Figure 2 The Large Intestine

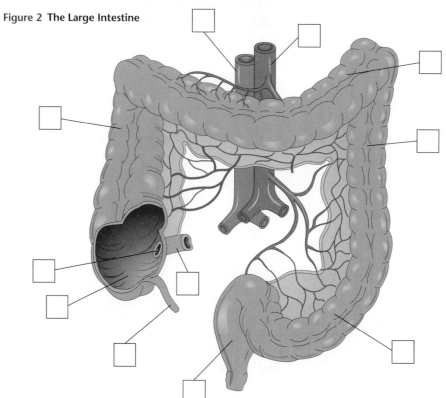

1. In which of the above organs is chyme produced?

2. In which organ of the digestive system does most of the chemical digestion and absorption of nutrients occur?

3. List each muscle or valve identified on the illustrations and specify into
   what organ it moves the digestive tract contents.

Color the Graphic

Color this illustration using the following color key. Then answer the questions that follow.

mouth – red
teeth – yellow
salivary glands – pink
pharynx – brown
esophagus – orange
liver – light green
gallbladder – dark green
stomach – light blue
pancreas – purple
small intestine – dark blue
large intestine – black

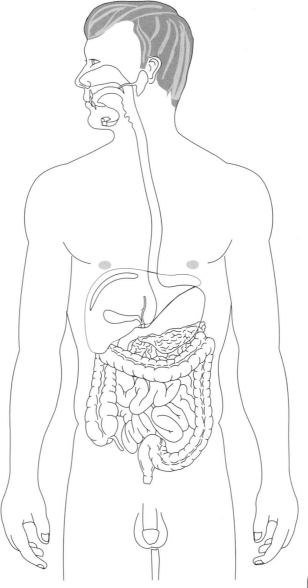

1. Which digestive system components allow for mastication?

2. The site of digestive enzyme production includes which components?

3. Which component produces bile?

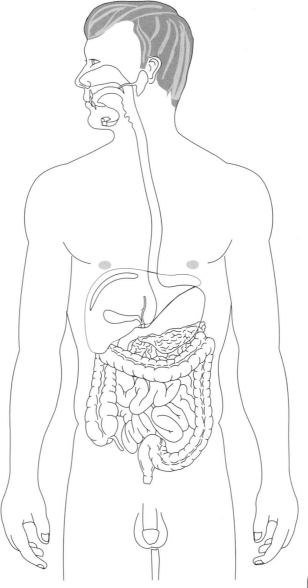**A.D.A.M.** Education

For additional information on common conditions associated with the digestive system, click on the Clinical Illustrations tab in A.D.A.M. Interactive Anatomy and narrow your search by choosing *Digestive* from the Body System menu. A quick search will lead you to a variety of images to explore, including an overview of the digestive system organs, gallstones, diverticulitis, GERD, hiatal hernia, irritable bowel disease, and colon cancer.

Additional Practice: The Digestive System

Identify the location of each of the terms listed above the image. Write the name of the anatomical part on the corresponding line beneath the image.

1. Mouth, Pharynx, and Esophagus

esophagus	laryngopharynx	oropharynx
nasopharynx	soft palate	hard palate
uvula	epiglottis	

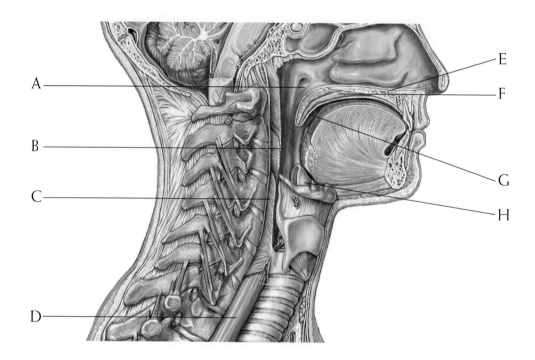

A. _____   E. _____

B. _____   F. _____

C. _____   G. _____

D. _____   H. _____

2. Salivary Glands

parotid gland
submandibular gland

parotid duct
sublingual gland

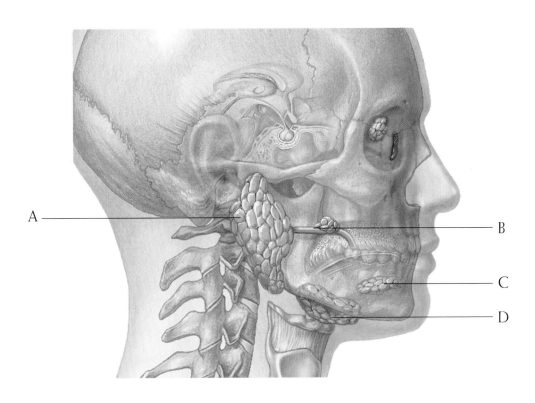

A. _____   C. _____

B. _____   D. _____

3. Frontal Stomach

cardiac part of
    stomach
pyloric part of
    stomach
jejunum

gastric rugae
greater curvature of
    stomach
pyloric sphincter

lesser curvature of
    stomach
duodenum

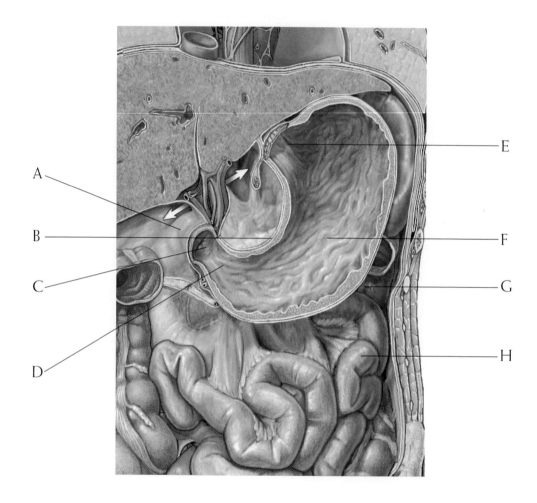

A. _____

B. _____

C. _____

D. _____

E. _____

F. _____

G. _____

H. _____

4. Small Intestine

pyloric sphincter   duodenum
ileum   jejunum

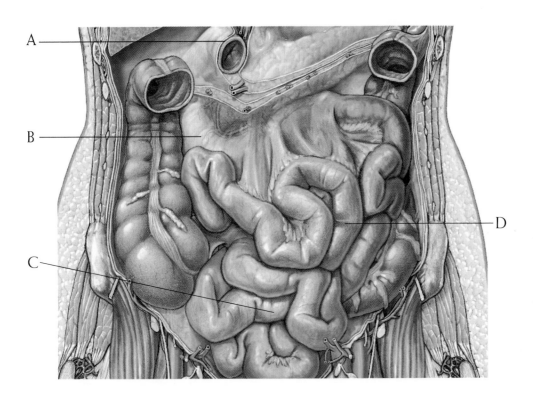

A. _____   C. _____

B. _____   D. _____

5. Large Intestine

cecum
transverse colon
sigmoid colon

ascending colon
left (splenic) flexure
rectum

right (hepatic) flexure
descending colon

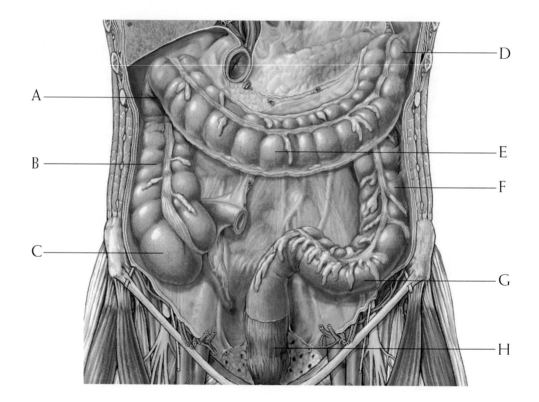

A. _____

B. _____

C. _____

D. _____

E. _____

F. _____

G. _____

H. _____

6. Anal Canal

anus   anal column   middle rectal fold/valve
rectum   sigmoid colon   superior rectal fold/valve
inferior rectal fold/valve   external anal sphincter

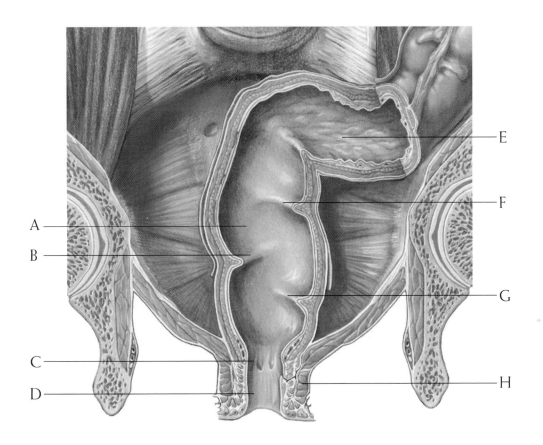

A. _____   E. _____

B. _____   F. _____

C. _____   G. _____

D. _____   H. _____

7. Bile Ducts

accessory pancreatic duct
hepatopancreatic ampulla/ampulla of Vater

common bile duct
major duodenal papilla/sphincter of Oddi

cystic duct
main pancreatic duct
common hepatic duct
gallbladder

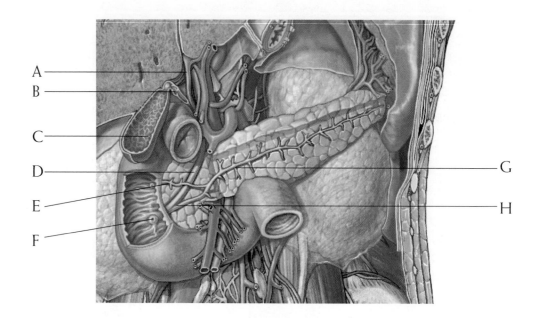

A. _____   E. _____

B. _____   F. _____

C. _____   G. _____

D. _____   H. _____

8. Liver and Gallbladder

falciform ligament
inferior vena cava
round ligament of liver

right lobe of liver
left lobe of liver
gallbladder

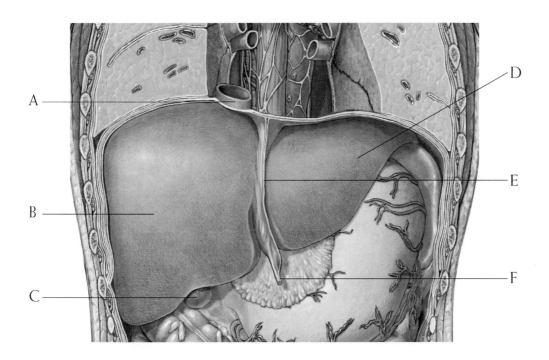

A. _____   D. _____

B. _____   E. _____

C. _____   F. _____

9. Liver (Inf)

bile duct   gallbladder   quadrate lobe of liver
portal vein   right lobe of liver left lobe of liver
hepatic artery   caudate lobe of liver

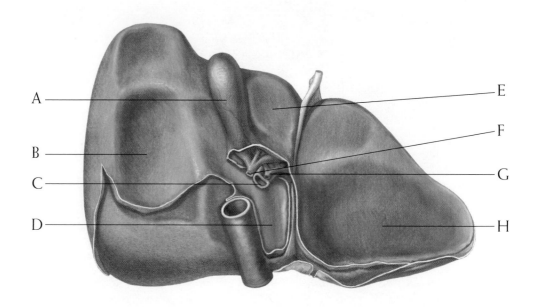

A. _____   E. _____

B. _____   F. _____

C. _____   G. _____

D. _____   H. _____

10. Digestive Process

Ingestion   Propulsion   Mechanical digestion
Chemical digestion   Absorption   Defecation

_____ is the introduction of food into the GI tract.

_____ is the moving of food along the GI tract with alternating muscle contractions.

_____ is the mixing and breaking down food into smaller fragments without disrupting chemical bonds.

_____ is the breaking down large food molecules to their building blocks by enzymes.

_____ is the transport of digested end products from the GI tract into the blood or lymph.

_____ is the elimination of indigestible residues from the GI tract via the anus.

11. Anatomy I

mouth   stomach   small intestine   pancreas

The _____ is the initial site for carbohydrate digestion.

The _____ is the initial site for protein digestion.

The _____ is the primary site for fat digestion.

The _____ has both exocrine and endocrine functions.

12. Anatomy II

small intestine   large intestine   liver   gallbladder

The _____ is the major site for nutrient absorption.

The _____ is the major site for water absorption.

The _____ is responsible for producing bile.

The _____ is the major storage site for bile.

13. Digestion

Amylase   Pepsin   Lipase   Bile

_____ is responsible for initiating carbohydrate digestion.

_____ is responsible for initiating protein digestion.

_____ is responsible for the majority of fat digestion.

_____ acts as an emulsifying agent before fat digestion can begin.

14. Digestive Tract

mucosa   submucosa   muscularis   serosa

The _____ layer of the digestive tract comes in direct contact with undigested food.

The _____ layer of the digestive tract contains blood vessels, lymphatic vessels, and glands.

The _____ layer of the digestive tract is responsible for peristalsis.

The _____ is the outer layer of the digestive tract.

Practical Application

Write brief responses to the following scenarios.

1. Explain the anatomical reasons why ingested food can be expelled through the nose or pass into the respiratory passages instead of entering the esophagus.

2. Describe how surgically blocking off a portion of the stomach can aid in weight loss. Why would blocking off or removing a portion of the small intestine also cause a person to lose weight?

3. What is the physiological cause of the increased flatulence that lactose-intolerant people experience when they drink milk?

4. The hormone changes that accompany pregnancy result in the relaxation of certain smooth muscles in the body. How is this related to the heart-burn that many women experience when they are pregnant?

5. The presence of fat in chyme stimulates the production of cholecysto-kinin (CCK). Why would a diet totally void of fat have an effect on the digestion of other nutrients?

6. The bacterium *Helicobacter pylori* can penetrate the mucosal lining of the stomach and, in doing so, damage mucus-producing cells. How does this contribute to ulcer formation?

7. Explain the effects that abnormal peristalsis in the colon could have on the digestive system.

8. In which abdominopelvic quadrant would a person experiencing impaction (buildup of fecal matter) in the sigmoid colon experience tenderness? In which quadrant would an individual with gallstones most likely experience tenderness?

9. The genetic disease cystic fibrosis results from a gene that codes for a protein that forms chloride-ion channels. Although the most obvious symptoms of this disease occur in the respiratory system due to abnormal buildup of mucus, the abnormal protein produced by an individual afflicted with this disease also impairs the function of certain secretory cells in the pancreas. Secretions produced by affected cells are very thick and viscous. How would this affect the exocrine function of the pancreas?

10. List three ways in which the nervous system is involved in digestive system function.

Laboratory Activity 1

Microscopic Identification of Normal Digestive Organs

Background

Looking at microscopic preparations of digestive system structures helps scientists to better understand how the various organs function. Many physicians and scientific researchers investigate organ function by reviewing photographs of tissues kept in databases. They can access the databases to view specimens that are not readily available to them, and they can share the images with colleagues around the world, allowing them to help each other with a variety of medical investigations.

Materials

- Internet access
- Printer
- White drawing paper
- Yellow highlighter marker
- Orange highlighter marker
- Green highlighter marker

Procedure and Analysis

Go to http://anatphys.emcp.net/BUHistology. Click on the *Digestive System: Alimentary Canal* link. Follow the instructions for each of the activities listed.

Esophagus Click on the link for the esophagus. Study the image and click to view the labeled diagram. Note the relative proportions of mucosa, muscle layers, and any visible glandular tissues. Print out the labeled image and use the highlighters to color the following structures: mucosa=yellow, muscle=orange, and glandular tissues=green.

Stomach Look at the stomach specimens by clicking on the fundic stomach (H and E) and pyloric stomach I (H and E) links. H and E (hematoxylin and eosin) is the type of staining technique used to color molecules in the cell. Note the relative proportions of mucosa, muscle layers, and any visible glandular tissues between the two stomach sections. Print out the labeled image and use the highlighters to color the following structures: mucosa=yellow, muscle=orange, and glandular tissues=green. Compare each stomach section to the diagram of the esophagus. Note the differences and similarities. Which stomach section most closely resembles the esophagus?

Small Intestine Click on the links leading to the images jejunum I (eosin and toluidine blue), ileum I, villi (H and E), ileum I, and Peyer's patches (H and E). How do the sections of intestine vary from each other? Print out the labeled image and use the highlighters to color the following structures: mucosa=yellow, muscle=orange, and glandular tissues=green. Compare each section to the diagram of the stomach. Note the differences and similarities.

Large Intestine and Rectum Look at the images of the appendix (H and E), colon (H and E), and anal canal (H and E). Compare the sections, and note the differences and similarities. Print out the labeled image and use the highlighters to color the following structures: mucosa=yellow, muscle=orange, and glandular tissues=green. Compare these sections to the images of the small intestine. Note the differences and similarities.

A good way to review the images is to have a classmate print out the unlabeled images and see if you can identify the organ and its particular features.

Laboratory Activity 2

Effects of Antacids on Protein Digestion

Background

Antacids are a common over-the-counter remedy used by many people to treat reflux and upset stomach. They reduce the acidity of the stomach contents, thereby reducing the corrosive effects of the acid on the esophagus and stomach. The overall effectiveness of antacids is debatable, and some physicians believe there are risks involved with taking them. Taking too many antacids can cause digestive system problems, especially in combination with a high-protein meal. Information about the chemistry of antacids can be obtained by searching the term "antacids" on the National Institutes of Health website at http://anatphys.emcp.net/MedlinePlus. This activity investigates the effects of antacids on the digestion of egg-white protein.

Materials

- Seven 1/2-inch square cubes of egg white from a soft-boiled egg
- 1% pepsin solution
- 0.8% hydrochloric acid solution
- 0.5% baking soda (sodium bicarbonate) solution
- Two types of antacid pills, each ground into separate containers holding 100 mL of distilled water
- Distilled water
- Six calibrated droppers for transferring the different solutions
- Three droppers for collecting samples of epinephrine, caffeine, and coffee or tea
- Seven clean, large test tubes
- Test-tube rack
- Strips of universal pH paper
- Forceps
- Water bath or incubator set at 37°C
- One sheet of lined notebook paper

Procedure

This activity involves setting up a series of conditions that model the chemical environment of the stomach. Scientists use experiments like this one to better understand the chemical reactions that take place during digestion. This experiment models the effects of antacids on protein digestion. Carry out the following steps to conduct this experiment:

1. Write out a table of the setup to use for recording data. (Your table should look similar to the example below.)

Table 13.1 Data Recording Example

Tube #	1	2	3	4	5	6	7
5-minute Observation							
10-minute Observation							
15-minute Observation							
20-minute Observation							
25-minute Observation							
Solution pH							
Appearance of egg white at 30 minutes							

2. Label the test tubes from 1 to 7, and place them in the rack in numerical order.
3. Place a square of egg white into each tube.
4. Add the various chemicals based on the instructions in Table 13.2. Use separate droppers for the water, baking soda, antacid, hydrochloric acid, and pepsin solutions.

Table 13.2 Test-Tube Setup Grid

Tube Number	Water (mL)	Baking Soda (mL)	Antacid (mL)	Hydrochloric Acid (mL)	Pepsin Solution (mL)
1	15				
2	12				3
3	12			3	
4	9			3	3
5	6	3		3	3
6	6		3	3	3
7	6		3	3	3

5. Place the rack of test tubes into a water bath or incubator set at 37°C.
6. Gently shake the tubes every 5 minutes for 25 minutes. Record the consistency of the egg white cubes each time after shaking the tubes.
7. Observe the egg white after 30 minutes and record your observations.
8. Test the pH of each tube by placing the tip of a pH strip into each one. Use a separate strip for each tube. Record the pH of each solution on the data sheet.

9. Record the appearance of the egg white in each tube on the data sheet. Compare the egg white in tubes 2 through 7 with the egg white in test tube 1.

Analysis

Answer the following questions:

1. What effect does pepsin alone (test tube 2) have on the digestion of proteins?
2. What effect does hydrochloric acid alone (test tube 3) have on the digestion of proteins?
3. How effective was the digestion of egg white in test tube 4, which modeled the normal human stomach?
4. What effects did baking soda have on the digestion of protein in the model stomach?
5. What effects did the different antacids have on the digestion of protein in the model stomach?
6. Describe the relationship between pH and the digestion of protein.
7. How would you use this experiment to explain the possible negative health effects of antacids?

 Quiz

1. Which of the following is *not* a component of the digestive tract?
   a) mouth
   b) pancreas
   c) stomach
   d) intestines

2. Embryological digestive system tissues are formed through:
   a) blastulation
   b) peristalsis
   c) gastrulation
   d) meiosis

3. Malformation of the tongue could be described as a(n):
   a) lobular disorder
   b) pharyngeal abnormality
   c) uvular disorder
   d) lingual anomaly

4. When a child has lost his two front teeth, which type of teeth are missing?
   a) molars
   b) incisors
   c) cuspids
   d) bicuspids

5. If an ulcer is described as involving only the most superficial layer of the digestive tract, it is located in the:
   a) muscularis layer
   b) mucosa
   c) serosa
   d) All of the above

6. Acid reflux could cause damage to the:
    a) esophagus
    b) pharynx
    c) throat
    d) All of the above

7. Cells in the stomach produce:
    a) hydrochloric acid
    b) proteases
    c) gastrin
    d) All of the above

8. Microvilli are projections on the epithelial cells lining the:
    a) small intestine
    b) stomach
    c) large intestine
    d) All of the above

9. Which of the following types of cells would *not* be found in the small intestine?
    a) paneth cells
    b) enterocytes
    c) enteroendocrine
    d) acini

10. Which of the following is true about zymogens?
    a) They are produced only in the small intestine.
    b) They are active enzymes.
    c) They are transported by the pancreatic and common bile ducts.
    d) All of the above

11. Which of the following describes the liver?
    a) It has four lobes.
    b) It produces bile.
    c) It is capable of regeneration.
    d) All of the above

12. Which of the following is *not* a function of the liver?
    a) formation of serum globulins
    b) production of digestive enzymes
    c) breakdown of amino acids
    d) synthesis of heparin

13. Diet pills that help to control the sensation of hunger would most likely have a direct effect on:
    a) bile production
    b) the colon
    c) the hypothalamus
    d) peristalsis

14. Cholecystokinin stimulates:
    a) pancreatic enzyme production
    b) hydrochloric acid production by the stomach
    c) bicarbonate production by the pancreas
    d) All of the above

15. Which of the following is absorbed in the stomach?
    a) amino acids and lipids
    b) glucose
    c) alcohol and drugs
    d) All of the above

16. The site of most chemical digestion and absorption is the:
    a) small intestine
    b) stomach
    c) large intestine
    d) All of the above

17. Most fluids and electrolytes are transferred from the digestive tract to the blood stream in the:
    a) small intestine
    b) stomach
    c) large intestine
    d) All of the above

18. Which of the following is *not* true of the hepatic portal system?
    a) It transfers bile to the small intestine.
    b) It allows absorbed nutrients to be further "processed" before entering general circulation.
    c) It transports blood from the digestive tract to the liver.
    d) It allows removal of many toxic substances.

19. The bicarbonate component of pancreatic fluid:
    a) chemically digests food
    b) is produced in response to CCK
    c) increases the pH of chyme
    d) All of the above

20. Which of the following is true of *Salmonella?*
    a) It is linked to ulcer formation.
    b) It is a virus.
    c) It can cause inflammatory bowel disease.
    d) It is a common cause of food poisoning.

21. A scar resulting from an appendectomy (removal of the appendix) would be found:
    a) in the upper right quadrant
    b) in the lower right quadrant
    c) in the upper left quadrant
    d) in the lower left quadrant

22. Colon polyps are:
    a) not a very common disorder
    b) often associated with diets high in fat and low in fiber
    c) always considered to be a serious health threat
    d) All of the above

23. The segment of the colon located between the hepatic and splenic flexure
    is the _____ colon.
    a) descending
    b) ascending
    c) sigmoid
    d) transverse

24. Starch digestion begins in the:
    a) stomach
    b) mouth
    c) duodenum
    d) jejunum

25. Age-related decline in liver and gallbladder function results in decreased
    digestion of:
    a) proteins
    b) starches
    c) fats
    d) All of the above

CHAPTER

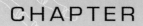

14

THE URINARY SYSTEM

Introduction

The urinary system helps maintain homeostasis by filtering the blood and ridding the body of metabolic wastes in the form of urine. The urinary system also regulates pH levels in conjunction with the respiratory system and works with the endocrine system to regulate electrolyte balance and the water content of the blood. The following exercises will help you apply what you have learned about the urinary system and its complex network of filters. Refer to Chapter 14 of *Applied Anatomy & Physiology, A Case Study Approach* for assistance, if necessary. Access A.D.A.M. Interactive Anatomy for additional information on the concepts presented in the textbook.

Completion

Complete the following sentences by filling in each blank with a key term from the text.

1. The _____ are the organs that actually form urine, while the _____, _____ _____, and _____ are the organs and structures that form the conduction system that carries it out of the body.

2. Each kidney is surrounded by a cushion of fat called the _____ _____. It is secured to the abdominal wall by a connective-tissue covering called the _____ _____, and it has a concave indentation known as the _____, which is the entry point for the _____ _____ and the exit for the _____ _____ and _____.

3. Within the kidneys, urine is formed in the microscopic physiological units called _____, and is transported to the internal storage cavity of the kidneys, or _____ _____, through extensions called _____.

4. The nephron is composed of _____ _____ that expand to form _____ capsule. Within the capsule is the folded capillary called the _____. The structure formed by the latter two components is called the _____ _____.

5. The tubular arrangement of the nephron has four major segments: 1) the
_____ _____ _____; 2) the _____
_____ _____; 3) the _____ _____
_____; and 4) the _____ _____.

6. Urine formation can be thought of as a three-step process:
1) _____ _____; 2) _____ _____; and
3) _____ _____.

7. Most reabsorption occurs in the proximal convoluted tubule by a combination of _____ _____ (osmosis and facilitated diffusion)
and _____ _____ (pumping).

8. The transfer of many ions from the blood stream into the _____
through the process of _____ _____ helps to maintain a
desirable body fluid pH.

9. _____ _____ and _____ are both hormones
that aid in water retention in the renal tubules, while the hormone
_____ _____ _____ causes diuresis.

10. Swelling of the glomerular membranes is known as _____. It can
be categorized on the basis of symptoms as being a urinary system disorder of _____.

Matching

Match each of the following terms with the corresponding description by placing the letter of the term in on the blank next to the correct description.

a) anuria

b) caliculi

c) diuresis

d) external urethral
sphincter

e) filtrate

f) hemodialysis

g) internal urinary
sphincter

h) micturition

i) polyuria

j) renal columns

k) renal pyramids

l) retroperitoneal

m) symported

n) urethral orifice

o) water conservation

_____ water excretion from the body

_____ collected in the renal corpuscle

_____ moved by carrier proteins

_____ point of exit from the body for urine

_____ triangular-shaped medullar tissue

_____ voluntary muscular ring

_____ kidney stones

_____ urine voiding

_____ behind the lining of the abdominal cavity

_____ reabsorption in the collecting tube

_____ excess urine production

_____ extensions of the cortex

_____ artificial blood-filtering procedure

_____ involuntary muscular ring

_____ lack of urine production

Complete the Terms Table

Fill in the missing key terms and/or definitions in the following table.

Term	Definition
	a capillary loop within the nephron
	loss of the voluntary control of holding urine in the bladder
urinary retention	
	abnormal loss of fluid from the body
urine concentration	
	the process by which plasma and many dissolved substances are moved from the blood into Bowman's capsule
tubular reabsorption	
	the process by which certain waste products and ions are removed from the blood into the tubular fluid
	hormone secreted by special cardiac cells that functions to lower blood volume and blood pressure
polycystic kidney disease	
	irreparable nephron damage and loss of kidney function
cystocele	

Label the Graphic

Identify each of the following terms in the illustrations on the next page. Write the number of the anatomical part in the box indicating its location. Then answer the questions that follow.

1. abdominal aorta
2. adrenal glands
3. calyces
4. external urinary meatus (orifice)
5. inferior vena cava
6. left kidney
7. medulla (renal pyramid)
8. renal artery
9. renal cortex
10. renal pelvis
11. renal vein
12. right kidney
13. ureter
14. urethra
15. urinary bladder

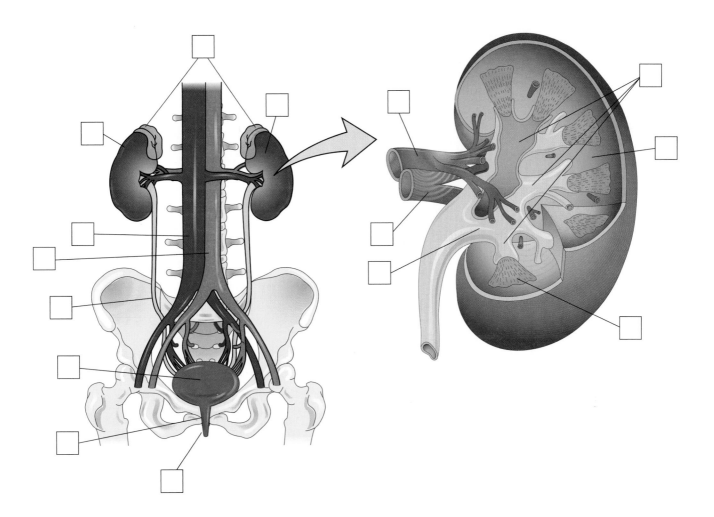

1. What hormone do the adrenal glands produce that influences urine formation?

2. Name one of the blood vessels shown above that returns blood to the heart after it has been filtered by the kidneys.

3. Through which of the illustrated blood vessels is blood that is to be filtered by the kidneys carried?

Color the Graphic

Color this illustration using the following color key. Then answer the questions that follow.

arteries – red
veins – blue
glomerulus – pink
Bowman's capsule – yellow
proximal convoluted tubule – orange
descending loop of Henle – light green
ascending loop of Henle – dark green
distal convoluted tubule – brown
collecting tubule – black

1. What two structures are the structural components of the renal corpuscle?

2. What physiological step of urine formation occurs in the renal corpuscle?

3. What physiological steps of urine formation occur in all areas of the peritubular capillary system?

4. In what structure does the majority of urine concentration occur?

Additional Practice: The Urinary System

Identify the location of each of the terms listed above the image. Write the name of the anatomical part on the corresponding line beneath the image.

1. Kidney I

renal cortex   renal medulla   renal pyramid
renal column   minor calyx   major calyx
renal pelvis   ureter

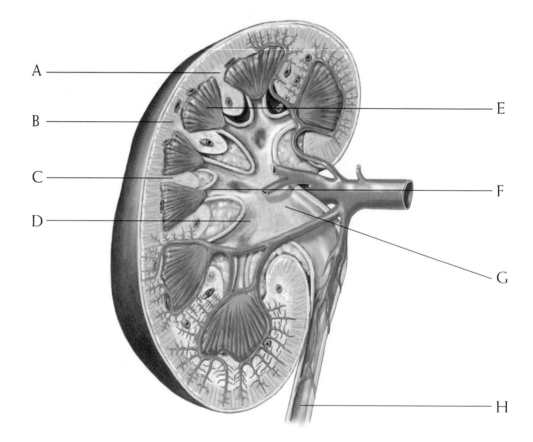

A. _____   E. _____

B. _____   F. _____

C. _____   G. _____

D. _____   H. _____

2. Nephron

glomerulus
descending limb of
   loop of Henle
peritubular capillary

proximal convoluted
   tubule
collecting tubule

distal convoluted tubule
ascending limb of loop
   of Henle

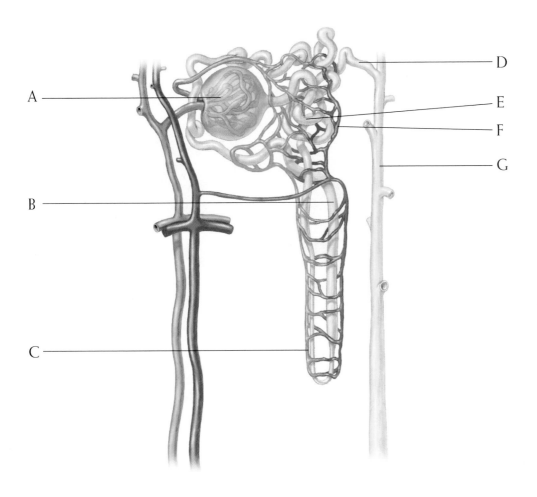

A. _____

B. _____

C. _____

D. _____

E. _____

F. _____

G. _____

3. Female Urinary (Med)

ureter
orifice of ureter / opening of ureter
anus

urinary bladder
urethra
uterus

pubic symphysis
vagina

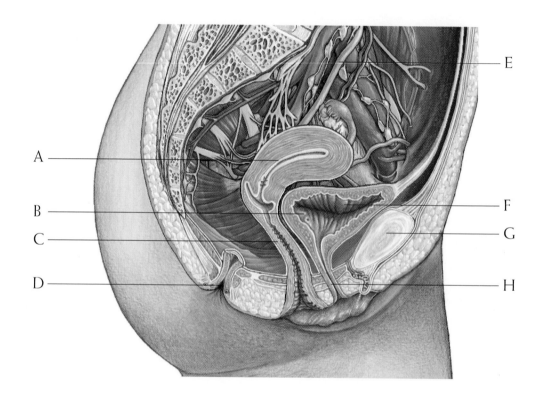

A. _____   E. _____

B. _____   F. _____

C. _____   G. _____

D. _____   H. _____

4. Male Urinary (Med)

orifice of ureter/opening
    of ureter
external meatus of
    urethra / urinary meatus

urinary bladder
spongy part of urethra

prostatic part of urethra
membranous part of
    urethra

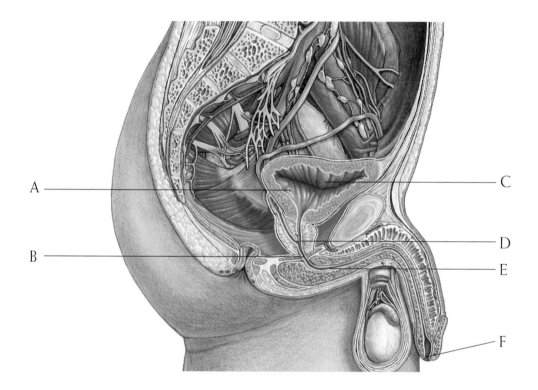

A. _____   D. _____

B. _____   E. _____

C. _____   F. _____

5. Anatomy

ureter   kidney   bladder   urethra

The _____ connects the kidney to the bladder.

The _____ serves as a storage tank for urine.

The _____ drains the bladder of urination.

The _____ contains the nephrons responsible for filtering blood.

6. Urine I

Urgency   Incontinence   Frequency   Retention

_____ is a feeling when it is necessary to void the bladder of urine.

_____ is the frequent voiding of small amounts of urine.

_____ is a condition where the bladder is unable to expel urine.

_____ is a condition when a person is unable to voluntarily control the external urethral sphincter.

7. Kidney II

pyramid   cortex   calyx   renal pelvis

A triangular structure found in the renal medulla is called a

_____.

The collecting ducts of the nephrons drain into a small space called a

_____.

The large, funnel-shaped chamber that drains into the ureter is called the

_____.

The outer layer of the kidney containing the majority of nephrons is the

_____.

8. Blood Supply

renal artery   afferent arteriole   glomerulus   peritubular

The _____ supplies blood to the kidney.

The _____ is the site for the filtration of blood.

The _____ capillaries collect reabsorbed fluid from the renal tubules.

The _____ delivers blood to the glomerulus.

9. Bladder

detrusor   internal urethral   trigone   external urethral

The _____ muscle contracts to push urine out of the bladder.

The _____ is the triangular region of the bladder between the openings for the ureters and urethra.

The _____ sphincter is voluntary and made of skeletal muscle.

The _____ sphincter is involuntary and made of smooth muscle.

10. Urine II

glycosuria   ketonuria   pyuria   hematuria

The presence of sugar in the urine is known as _____.

The presence of pus in the urine is known as _____.

The presence of blood in the urine is known as _____.

The presence of ketone bodies in the urine is known as _____.

Practical Application

Write brief responses to the following scenarios.

1. Describe one way in which the urinary system affects the pH regulation of the respiratory system.

2. Briefly discuss one way in which the urinary system affects the circulatory system.

3. Since the influence of one organ system over another is usually a reciprocal relationship, briefly discuss one way in which the circulatory system directly affects the urinary system.

4. Describe a role that the skeletal system plays in the urinary system.

5. You learned about the role that the endocrine system plays in urinary system function in Chapter 14 of the textbook, but can you think of a way that the urinary system provides for the endocrine system?

6. Explain how the abnormal amount of proteins that victims of severe burns lose through the surface of their skin contributes to edema and dehydration.

7. How does the anatomical location of the ureter-bladder connection point aid in the ability of the bladder to act as a reservoir for urine?

8. How would hyperkalemia (high blood-potassium levels) influence diuresis?

9. Specific gravity is a measurement that indicates the density of a fluid compared with that of water. Water is said to have a specific gravity of 1. Any addition of solute will increase the specific gravity. Because urine is not pure water, and contains many dissolved substances, its normal specific gravity is greater than 1. What effect would a decrease in ADH have on diuresis, and how would this affect the specific gravity of urine?

10. Why are hypertensive patients encouraged to restrict the amount of salt they consume?

Urine Chemical Analysis

Background

Urinalysis, or chemical analysis of urine, can be used to test for certain metabolic products and blood components—the presence of which can indicate pathologies or other abnormal body functions. Measurements such as pH and specific gravity can also be ascertained through urinalysis. Various types of urinalysis reagent strips, used for quick chemical analysis of urine samples, are now available commercially, and have replaced the more labor-intensive tests used in the past. In this activity, you will use urinalysis reagent strips to test urine. Although you will use artificial urine in this activity and will not need to take contamination precautions, in the testing of real urine it is imperative that samples are collected and analyzed in a prescribed manner to avoid contamination. Each student group will record measurements for pH, glucose, protein, ketones, and blood on three artificial urine samples and compare their results with normal values. Each group must also determine possible pathologies for any abnormal samples.

Materials

- Three artificial urine samples, labeled A, B, and C
- Protective gloves (optional; check with your instructor)
- Beaker of disinfectant (optional; check with your instructor)
- Three urinalysis reagent chemical test strips and corresponding color chart
- Clock with a second hand
- Urinalysis handbook or computer with Internet access

Procedure

1. Dip one urinalysis test strip into urine sample A. Make sure all the test strip squares are submerged.
2. Quickly remove the strip and run it along the top of the test tube to remove excess liquid.
3. Hold the strip over a paper towel with the longer side parallel to the ground. This will allow any excess urine to drain off without causing it to run from one test square to another. Check the color chart to determine the appropriate amount of time to wait before reading the strip, and begin timing.
4. After the appropriate amount of time has passed for each test, compare the colors of the test squares for pH, protein, glucose, ketones, and blood with the corresponding color chart, and record the values in Table 14.1. Be sure to record units of measure as well as the numeric values.
5. If the test strip indicates the presence of blood, discard the strip in a beaker of disinfectant. If blood is not detected, discard the strip in a normal trash receptacle.
6. Repeat steps 1-5 for samples B and C. Make sure to use a new test strip for each sample.

Table 14.1 **Recorded Values**

Sample	pH	Protein	Glucose	Ketone	Blood
A					
B					
C					

7. Using the resource material provided by your instructor (i.e. a urinalysis handbook or a website such as http://anatphys.emcp.net/TXUrinalysis), fill in the normal values for each of the chemical test results in Table 14.2. (Hint: If you use the website suggested above, you can find a summary of normal values by accessing Activity 2.2 in the Chemical Testing section of the sidebar menu on the left side of the page and viewing the worksheet in the Directions section.)

Table 14.2 **Normal Urine Values**

Sample	pH	Protein	Glucose	Ketone	Blood	Possible Pathology
normal values						n/a
A						
B						
C						

8. For each abnormal value obtained in samples A, B, and C, place an arrow in the corresponding cell in Table 14.2 to indicate whether the value is higher or lower than the normal value.
9. Complete the table by listing a possible pathology (if any) that might be indicated for each sample. Use the resource material provided by your instructor as a guide for determining possible pathologies.

Analysis

1. If a normal value obtained for any of the above urine components was expressed as a unit of weight/time (such as mg/day), would a test strip reading allow you to make an accurate comparison? Explain.
2. Is an abnormal pH reading always cause for alarm? Why or why not? What pH readings might indicate a problem, and what might this problem be?
3. What conditions might cause a temporary elevation of glucose?
4. Can health professionals use reagent test strips to detect whether or not intact RBCs are present in the urine? Explain.
5. What would be a probable diagnosis for a patient whose urine tests positive for nitrite levels and leukocyte esterase?

Laboratory Activity 2

Microscopic Examination of Urine Sediment

Background

Analysis of urine sediment can provide medical professionals with valuable information about the health of an individual and even help them to diagnose certain diseases. While regular urinalysis can be performed fairly easily using test strips (as you learned in Laboratory Activity 1), urine sediment analysis must be performed by skilled professionals. In this activity, you will use a website to learn about the normal components of urine sediment as well as a few components whose presence may indicate pathology. You will also view photographs of actual microscopic specimens to get a better idea of how these components appear during analysis.

Materials

- Computer with Internet access

Procedure

1. Open your web browser and navigate to the following web pages to see some of the components you might encounter while performing a urine sediment analysis:

   http://anatphys.emcp.net/Microorganism
   http://anatphys.emcp.net/casts
   http://anatphys.emcp.net/cells1
   http://anatphys.emcp.net/cells2
   http://anatphys.emcp.net/cells3
   http://anatphys.emcp.net/crystals

2. Create a chart like the one in Table 14.3. In the Type column, list one type of each component that can be found in urine sediment. Write a short description of it in the Description column.

Table 14.3 **Urine Sediment Analysis Notes**

Component	Type	Description	Possible Pathology
microorganisms			
mucus			
casts			
RBCs			
WBCs			
Epithelial cells			
crystals			

3. Once you have filled out the Type and Description columns in Table 14.3, research online to determine possible pathologies than could be indicated by the presence of these components in the urine. One website you may want to use is http://anatphys.emcp.net/MayoUrinalysis.
4. Record your findings in the Possible Pathology column in Table 14.3

Analysis

In a brief analytical paragraph, describe which components one might regularly see in a urine sediment analysis, and which components might be cause for alarm. Support your statement with information found during your research.

Quiz

1. Which of the following is *not* a function of the urinary system?
   a) maintenance of body pH
   b) maintenance of electrolyte balance
   c) immune regulation
   d) osmotic homeostasis

2. The ureters and urethra:
   a) alter the composition of the urine
   b) reabsorb water from the urine
   c) conduct urine out of the body
   d) All of the above

3. The renal pyramids are:
   a) located in the renal medulla
   b) the location of the urine collection tubules
   c) separated by renal columns
   d) All of the above

4. Which of the following is the correct sequence of urine transfer out of the kidney?
   a) calyces, collecting duct, renal pelvis, ureter
   b) collecting duct, calyces, renal pelvis, ureter
   c) renal pelvis, collecting duct, calyces, ureter
   d) collecting duct, renal pelvis, calyces, ureter

5. Voluntary control of micturition is provided by the:
   a) internal urinary sphincter
   b) urethral orifice
   c) external urinary sphincter
   d) All of the above

6. Which of the following gives the urinary bladder the ability to distend and act as a reservoir for urine?
   a) the arrangement of the detrusor muscle fibers
   b) the transitional epithelial lining
   c) the involuntary closure of the internal urinary sphincter
   d) All of the above

7. Females are more susceptible to bacterial urinary tract infections than males due to:
   a) hormonal differences
   b) the smaller size of the female bladder
   c) the length and location of the female urethra
   d) All of the above

8. Which of the following is *not* a term used to refer to abnormal urine production?
   a) polyuria
   b) urinary retention
   c) anuria
   d) None of the above

9. Blood is carried to the glomerulus by the:
   a) efferent arteriole
   b) afferent arteriole
   c) renal artery
   d) renal vein

10. Which of the following is true of the peritubular capillary system?
    a) It consists of the glomerulus and Bowman's capsule.
    b) It is the site of urine filtration.
    c) It is the part of the nephron distal to the renal corpuscle.
    d) All of the above

11. Which of the following describes a correct sequence in the tubular arrangement within the nephron?
    a) Bowman's capsule, proximal convoluted tubules, loop of Henle
    b) proximal convoluted tubules, loop of Henle, distal convoluted tubules
    c) loop of Henle, distal convoluted tubules, collecting duct
    d) All of the above

12. Urine filtration occurs in the:
    a) renal corpuscle
    b) afferent arteriole
    c) loop of Henle
    d) collecting duct

13. Tubular reabsorption:
    a) occurs in the peritubular capillary system
    b) returns water, nutrients, and electrolytes to the blood
    c) is somewhat influenced by hormones
    d) All of the above

14. Which of the following is *not* a true statement about tubular secretion?
    a) It removes waste products from the blood.
    b) It aids in homeostasis of body pH.
    c) It elevates blood glucose levels.
    d) It contributes to urine electrolyte levels.

15. Urine concentration occurs in which part of the nephron?
    a) the glomerulus
    b) the proximal convoluted tubule
    c) the collecting duct
    d) All of the above

16. Water moves out of the collecting duct due to:
    a) the effects of antidiuretic hormone on its wall permeability
    b) the concentration gradient that exists between the tubular fluid and the interstitial fluid of the kidney medulla
    c) osmosis
    d) All of the above

17. High blood-potassium levels would stimulate the production of:
    a) antidiuretic hormone
    b) aldosterone
    c) atrial natriuretic factor
    d) angiotensin II

18. Which of the following hormones does *not* exert its effect on the nephron peritubular system?
    a) antidiuretic hormone
    b) aldosterone
    c) atrial natriuretic factor
    d) angiotensin II

19. Which of the following hormones would increase the water content of the urine?
    a) antidiuretic hormone
    b) aldosterone
    c) atrial natriuretic factor
    d) angiotensin II

20. Which of the following categories of urinary system diseases would *not* apply to polycystic kidney disease?
    a) infection
    b) genetic
    c) congenital
    d) degenerative

21. Which of the following types of inflammation does *not* occur in the conduction system components of the urinary system?
    a) cystitis
    b) urethritis
    c) pyelitis
    d) pyelonephritis

22. The presence of both proteinuria and hematuria may be indicative of:
    a) dysuria
    b) edema
    c) glomerulonephritis
    d) All of the above

23. Glucosuria and aminoaciduria:
    a) may lead to the formation of kidney or bladder calculi
    b) indicate normal urine values
    c) always indicate glucose and amino acid deficiencies
    d) have no effect on the osmolarity of the filtrate

24. Most malignancies in the urinary system:
    a) are ultimately fatal, even with early detection
    b) produce different symptoms than other urinary system disorders
    c) require the use of imaging techniques for definitive diagnosis
    d) All of the above

25. Most effects of urinary system aging are:
    a) the result of nephron function loss
    b) unrelated to the function of other body systems
    c) related to the increased incidence of disease that occurs with age
    d) All of the above

CHAPTER

15 THE REPRODUCTIVE SYSTEMS AND HUMAN DEVELOPMENT

Introduction

The reproductive system is designed to produce gametes, or sex cells, to ensure the continued propagation of the human species. The male reproductive organs produce sperm, and the female reproductive organs produce ova, or eggs. In addition to producing ova, the female reproductive system also nourishes the fertilized egg as it matures into a fetus capable of surviving on its own. The following exercises and lab activities will help you apply what you have learned about the structure and function of the reproductive system. If you need assistance, refer to Chapter 15 of *Applied Anatomy & Physiology, A Case Study Approach*. Additionally, you can access A.D.A.M. Interactive Anatomy for information that will expand your understanding of the concepts presented in the textbook.

Completion

Complete the following sentences by filling in each blank with a key term from the text.

1. Human sexual reproductive organs called _____ contain mobile cells called _____ _____ _____.

2. The organs of the female reproductive system that produce and transport the egg and developed fetus make up the _____ _____, which consists of the _____, _____ _____, _____, and _____.

3. The inner layer of the uterus is a thick mucosa called the _____, which is shed during the female's _____ _____.

4. The external genitalia of the female are collectively known as the _____, which consists of the fat pad covering the pubic bone, called the _____; the outer lips, called the _____ _____; and the inner lips, or _____ _____, which protect the sensitive erectile tissue known as the _____.

5. In the male, the tubes and glands that assist with the transport of sperm are called the _____ _____. The male's external genitalia consist of the _____ and _____.

6. Sperm maturation and storage occur in the _____. The sperm are then expelled into the _____ _____, where they mix with the fluid containing the enzymes, fructose, hormones, lipids, and proteins (produced by the _____ _____) that facilitate their survival. The combined mixture of sperm and this fluid is called _____, which is transferred to the vagina during sexual intercourse via the ejection process known as _____.

7. Blood enters the penis through the _____ _____ and enters the inner sheath of erectile tissue called the _____ _____, which prevents the urethra from closing the two outer chambers of erectile tissue called the _____ _____. This causes the penile enlargement and hardening known as a(n) _____.

8. The female sexual cycle, or _____ _____, can actually be thought of as two cycles (based on the major organs involved): the _____ cycle and the _____ cycle. The first prepares the egg for fertilization and can be further divided into the _____ and _____ phases, while the second involves the _____ _____, in which the endometrium thickens to prepare for pregnancy.

9. A fertilized egg is called a(n) _____. It divides to become a _____ as it travels down the fallopian tube to the uterus, where _____, or attachment to the endometrium, occurs. This induces the development of the nourishing organ called the _____. The fertilized egg then develops into a _____, and differentiation of tissues occurs. This is followed by continued growth until the fertilized egg finally becomes known as a _____.

10. When the placenta attaches to the lower part of the uterus, a condition known as _____ _____ results. This condition blocks the route of normal birth and usually requires surgical removal of the baby through the abdominal wall via a(n) _____ _____.

Matching

Match each of the following terms with the corresponding description by placing the letter of the term on the blank next to the correct description.

a) androgens

b) circumcision

c) copulation

d) Cowper's glands

e) ectopic

f) fimbriae

g) glans

h) lactation

i) oocyte

j) ovary

k) ovum

l) perineum

m) prostate gland

n) seminiferous tubules

o) testis

_____ milk production

_____ immature egg

_____ produces the mucus-like component of semen

_____ female gonad

_____ the tip of the penis

_____ produce the alkaline component of semen

_____ site of sperm production in the testes

_____ fingerlike oviduct projections

_____ surgical removal of the penis foreskin

_____ male gonad

_____ sexual intercourse

_____ aid in development of male sex characteristics

_____ describes a pregnancy outside of the uterus

_____ external area of the pelvic floor

_____ mature egg

Complete the Terms Table

Fill in the missing key terms and/or definitions in the following table.

Term	Definition
	developmental differences that distinguish the two genders
external genitalia	
	a fluid-filled sac in which an egg matures
corpus luteum	
	a condition in which it is not clear at birth whether the individual is a male or a female
lactiferous ducts	
	cells that produce testosterone in the testis
menses	
	an intense sensation that occurs at the height of sexual excitement
conception	
	a hormone produced by the placenta that maintains pregnancy; it is triggered by the release of estrogen and progesterone
	a fluid-filled sac that surrounds the fetus
hypospadia	
	cessation of the menstrual periods
andropause	

A.D.A.M. Education

For additional information on common conditions associated with the reproductive system, click on the Clinical Illustrations tab in A.D.A.M. Interactive Anatomy and then narrow your search by choosing *Reproductive* from the Body System menu. A quick search of each topic will lead you to a variety of images to explore, including *prostate cancer, testicular torsion, cesarean section, menstrual cycle, amniocentesis, mammography, breast anatomy, fibroids, placenta previa, fetal development,* and *cervical cancer.*

Label the Graphic

Identify each of the following terms in the illustrations on the next page. Write the number of the anatomical part in the box indicating its location. Then answer the questions that follow.

Figure 1 Terms

1. body of the uterus
2. cervix
3. fallopian tube
4. fundus of uterus
5. ovary
6. pubic bone
7. rectum
8. ureter
9. urethra
10. urinary bladder
11. vagina

Figure 2 Terms

1. anus
2. Cowper's (bulbourethral) gland
3. ductus (vas) deferens
4. epididymis
5. penis
6. prostate gland
7. rectum
8. scrotum
9. seminal vesicle
10. testis
11. ureter
12. urethra
13. urinary bladder

Figure 1 Female

Figure 2 Male

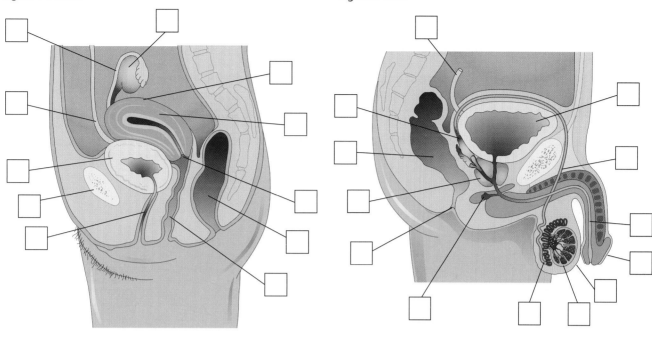

1. What structure carries the egg to the uterus?

2. Where does implantation normally take place?

3. Where are sperm produced?

4. What is the site of maturation and storage of sperm?

🌿A.D.A.M.Education

For an interactive experience with a three dimensional model of the reproductive organs, click on the 3D Anatomy tab within A.D.A.M. Interactive Anatomy and choose either the *3D Female Reproductive System* or the *3D Male Reproductive System* model. You will then be able to zoom, move, and turn the models to appreciate the anatomy from all views.

Color the Graphic

To view a series of animated presentations from the reproductive system, click on the Clinical Animations tab within A.D.A.M. Interactive Anatomy. Refine your search by choosing *Reproductive* from the Body System menu, clicking the search button, and then choosing from the following animations: *Egg cell production, Sperm production and pathway of ejaculation, Sexual differentiation, Menstrual cycle, Vasectomy, Enlarged prostate gland, Conception,* and *Fetal development.*

Color this illustration using the following color key. Then answer the questions that follow.

blastula entering uterus – light green
blastula implanting – dark green
embryo – purple
endometrium of uterine wall – pink
fallopian tube – yellow

fertilization – green
ovary – outline in black
ovulated egg – orange
uterine muscle wall – brown
zygote – blue

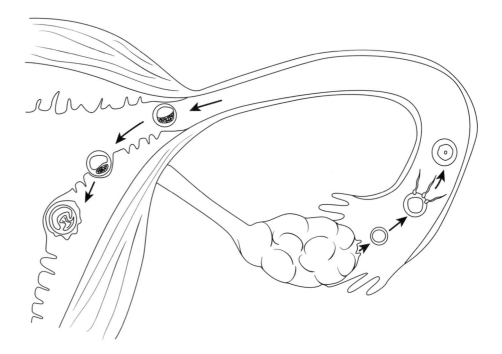

1. What is the name given to the stage of embryo tissue differentiation?

2. By what term is the developing embryo identified in the most advanced stages prior to birth?

292   CHAPTER 15

Additional Practice: The Reproductive Systems

Identify the location of each of the terms listed above the image. Write the name of the body part on the corresponding line beneath the image.

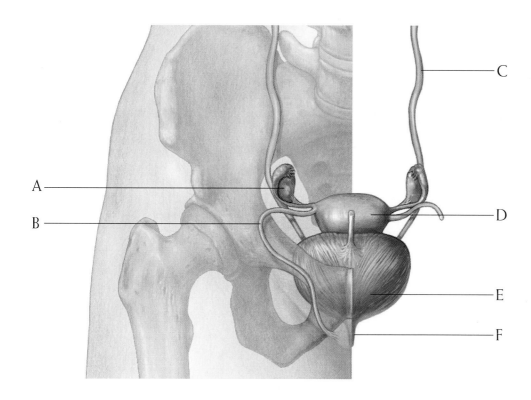

A.D.A.M. Education

For additional assistance on the labeling exercises, open A.D.A.M. Interactive Anatomy and click on the Atlas Anatomy tab. Next, refine your search by selecting *Reproductive* from the Body System menu and *Illustration* from the Image Type menu and then matching the images to the images in this section.

1. Female Pelvic Organs

ovary	round ligament of uterus	ureter
uterus	urinary bladder	urethra

A. _____   D. _____

B. _____   E. _____

C. _____   F. _____

2. Female Pelvic Organs (Lat)

left ovary   pubic symphysis   fundus of uterus
urinary bladder   vagina   labium minus
urethra   clitoris

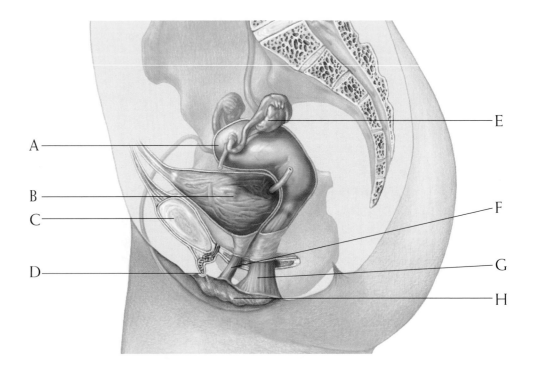

A. _____   E. _____

B. _____   F. _____

C. _____   G. _____

D. _____   H. _____

3. Female Pelvic Organs (Med)

uterine tube   myometrium   cervical canal
pubic symphysis   urethra   vagina
endometrium

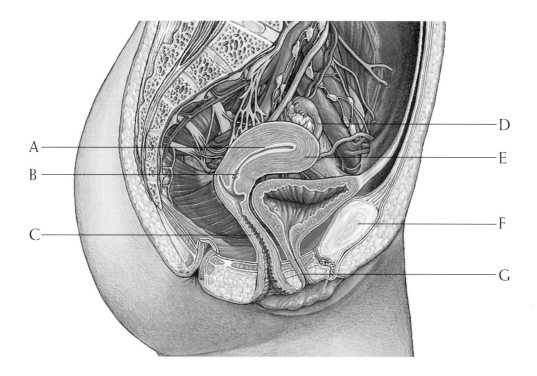

A. _____   E. _____

B. _____   F. _____

C. _____   G. _____

D. _____

4. Male Pelvic Organs (Lat)

corpus cavernosum   corpus spongiosum   ureter

seminal vesicle   prostate gland   ductus deferens

epididymis   testis

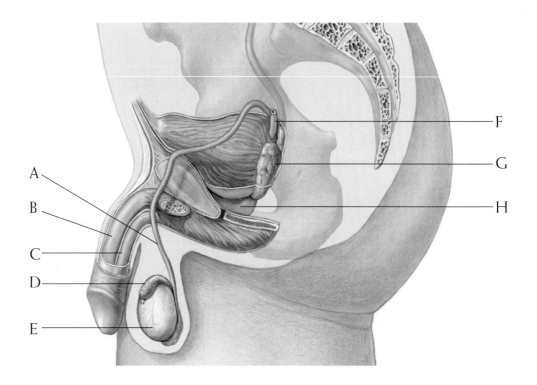

A. _____   E. _____

B. _____   F. _____

C. _____   G. _____

D. _____   H. _____

A.D.A.M. Education

5. Male Pelvic Organs (Med)

ductus deferens   prostate gland   urinary bladder
testis   epididymis
ejaculatory duct   seminal vesicle

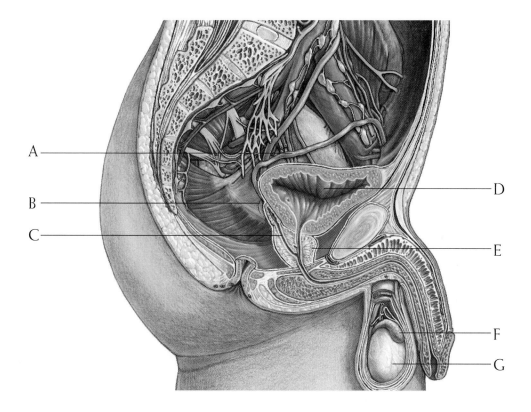

A. _____   E. _____

B. _____   F. _____

C. _____   G. _____

D. _____

6. Male Reproductive

circumcision	corpus spongiosum	impotence
scrotum	cryptorchidism	

_____ is the surgical removal of the foreskin (prepuce) from the glans penis.

_____ is a condition of undescended testes that can lead to sterility or cancer if not corrected.

_____ is the inability to either achieve or maintain an erection

The sac containing the testes is called the _____.

The singular part of the penis surrounding the penile urethra is the

_____.

Practical Application

Write brief responses to the following scenarios.

1. Describe the pathway that sperm travel from their site of production until they exit the body during ejaculation. Make sure to include the names of all relevant organs and structures of the male reproductive and urinary systems.

2. Describe how the anatomy of the female reproductive tract could lead to bacterial infection of the abdominal cavity.

3. List two enzymatic or hormonal abnormalities in a female that could cause her to develop male secondary sex characteristics.

4. Explain the physiological reason that wearing tight fitting underwear could contribute to a low sperm count in a male.

5. What effect could abnormally high levels of estrogen or testosterone in a pregnant female have on the developing fetus?

6. How are ectopic and tubal pregnancies possible?

7. Erectile dysfunction can be a result of improper neural stimulation. Which division of the nervous system is involved in this disorder, and how does it cause the inability to obtain an erection?

8. What role do the breasts play in reproduction?

9. What effect would a vasectomy or tubal ligation (surgical interruption of the fallopian tube pathway) have on normal hormone production and gamete formation?

10. Using your knowledge of the female menstrual cycle, explain the mathematics behind the statistic that females produce 350 to 500 ova throughout a normal life span.

> **✲A.D.A.M.** Education
>
> Click on the Encyclopedia tab of A.D.A.M. Interactive Anatomy to open the A.D.A.M. Multimedia Encyclopedia. A quick search of key terms from the textbook will help you reinforce the knowledge you have gained thus far. Try entering pathological terms such as *cervical cancer, breast cancer, fibroids, genital warts, ectopic pregnancy, prostate cancer, pelvic inflammatory disease (PID),* and *sexually transmitted disease (STD)* in the search bar to read more about these important topics dealing with the reproductive system.

Laboratory Activity 1

Predicting Birth Defects

Background

Physicians and scientists have amassed a great deal of detailed information about human embryological development. This information is stored in databases and image collections for use in understanding the causes of birth defects. The information is also a powerful tool for predicting the effects of chemicals on fetal development. Pathologists in particular use an understanding of embryology to better understand how certain drugs can affect a fetus. Today, it is common for attorneys and public health officials to use embryology databases to research incidents that have caused or could cause birth defects. This activity provides an embryology resource that can be used to predict the effects of particular drugs or pollutants on embryological development.

Materials

- Computer with Internet access
- Paper or spreadsheet software, such as Microsoft Excel, to use to record notes
- Access to a printer (if using spreadsheet software)

Procedure

Go to http://anatphys.emcp.net/VirtualHuman and familiarize yourself with the process of development from fertilization to the last week of pregnancy. Next, go to http://anatphys.emcp.net/VisibleEmbryo and review the different images representing the stages of human embryology.

Now, imagine that you are an attorney investigating the cases of four women who were exposed to a leak from an agricultural chemical plant near their homes while they were pregnant. The women are suing the chemical company because their children developed birth defects that they believe were caused by exposure to the chemicals leaked into the air. The women were not aware of the leak until public health officials noticed a string of mysterious illnesses in the area several months later. An Environmental Protection Agency (EPA) investigation found that the company recorded that the leak occurred, and that it was fixed within 24 hours, but that they never reported the leak to the community. The EPA investigation also discovered that the specific chemicals leaked were the pesticide aldrin and the fungicide dithiocarbamate. Your job is to determine whether the birth defects in these children were caused by either of the chemicals or by other unrelated factors. Use the Internet to research the nature of the pesticides, and the embryology websites (in conjunction with the information below) to investigate the state of the embryo at the time of the mothers' exposure.

Woman 1 She was one week pregnant when the incident occurred. Her boy was born one month premature and had underdeveloped lungs. Physicians discovered a septal defect in the boy's heart that had to be surgically corrected. The woman says that her two older children had no such problems.

Woman 2 Her physician confirms that she was six weeks pregnant at the time the chemicals were released. Her baby girl was born with facial defects that caused her eyes to be very far apart and her nose to be malformed. The girl also has fingers missing on one hand. The woman has no other children.

Woman 3 She says that she was eight weeks pregnant at the time of the chemical leak. Her baby girl was delivered prematurely with a condition called anencephaly. The child died three weeks after birth. The mother has one other child who was born with no problems.

Woman 4 Two physicians confirm that the woman was six months pregnant at the time of the incident. Her baby boy was born with genital deformations that prevented the fusion of his penis and scrotum. The defects were surgically corrected, but the boy may never have full use of his penis and may not be able to reproduce. The mother also has a two-year-old girl who was born with no problems.

Analysis

Within a chart or table, record the tissues or organ systems that were developing in each fetus at the time its mother was exposed to the chemicals. For each case, determine whether the chemical exposure could have been responsible for the birth defects. Also, predict what developmental defects could occur if a mother was exposed to these chemicals at one week, six weeks, eight weeks, and six months pregnant. In your analysis, think about how the chemical would reach the baby to produce damaging effects. Write a brief report in which you explain your conclusions and state whether each woman has enough evidence to blame the chemical company for her child's birth defects.

Laboratory Activity 2

Modeling the Test for Human Chorionic Gonadotropin

Background

Pregnancy testing attempts to determine whether human chorionic gonadotropin (hCG), a protein produced by a developing embryo, is present in a woman's body. Human chorionic gonadotropin maintains the corpus luteum and causes it to secrete progesterone, which ensures that the uterine lining is thick and has ample blood vessels to sustain the growth of the fetus. Physicians can collect hCG from blood or urine samples. Pregnancy testing commonly uses a technique called an immunoassay. The test uses antibodies that specifically bind to hCG, so if hCG is present, the antibodies stick to it and stimulate a chemical reaction that indicates a positive test. Many physicians use a sensitive test in which they look for a clump of material that falls out of solution. This clump is formed when the antibodies bind to the hCG. The clump looks like a fuzzy, white residue on the bottom of a test tube. In this activity you will be asked to interpret the results of three samples being tested for hCG.

Materials

- One bottle of red food coloring
- Distilled water
- Stock solutions
  - 3 g of calcium hydroxide in 200 mL (1.5%) of distilled water
  - 16 g of ammonium oxalate in 200 mL (8%) of distilled water containing four drops of red food coloring
  - 32 g of ammonium oxalate in 200 mL (16%) distilled water containing 4 drops of red food coloring
  - 200 mL of distilled water containing four drops of red food coloring

- Classroom set of solutions
  - Vials containing distilled water, labeled *Negative Control*
  - Vials containing the 8% ammonium oxalate solution, labeled *Positive Control*
  - Vials containing the distilled water and red food coloring solution, labeled *Sample 1*
  - Vials containing the 8% ammonium oxalate solution, labeled *Sample 2*
  - Vials containing the 16% ammonium oxalate solution, labeled *Sample 3*
  - Vials containing the 1.5% calcium hydroxide solution, labeled *hCG Test Solution*
- Six droppers for each lab group
- Five small test tubes for each lab group
- Marker (to label test tubes)
- Surgical gloves
- Computer with Internet access

Note It is recommended that you wear surgical gloves when handling the solutions. The samples should be handled as though they are actual human body fluids. All of the solutions can be stored in labeled bottles at room temperature for six months. Excess or waste solutions should be flushed down a drain.

Procedure

1. Place five test tubes in the test tube rack.
2. Label the tubes with the numbers 1 through 5.
3. Record the tube numbers on a sheet of paper.
4. Collect one vial each of hCG Test Solution, Positive Control, Negative Control, Sample 1, Sample 2, and Sample 3.
5. Add 10 drops of hCG Test Solution to each tube using a clean dropper.
6. Add 5 drops of Positive Control to test tube 1 using a clean dropper. Record the results.
7. Add 5 drops of Negative Control to test tube 2 using a clean dropper. Record the results.
8. Add 5 drops of Sample 1 to test tube 3 using a clean dropper. Record the results.
9. Add 5 drops of Sample 2 to test tube 4 using a clean dropper. Record the results.
10. Add 5 drops of Sample 3 to test tube 5 using a clean dropper. Record the results.

Analysis

1. What is the reason for using the positive and negative control samples?
2. What can you conclude about each sample?
3. How do you explain the differences between the Positive Control and Sample 3?
4. You just discovered that Sample 3 is a false-positive test result. Visit http://anatphys.emcp.net/WebMDPregTest to determine the possible causes of the false-positive test result seen in this sample.

Quiz

1. Which of the following is *not* related to puberty?
   a) development of secondary sex characteristics
   b) sexual dimorphism
   c) differentiation of gonads
   d) sexual reproductive capability

2. Mammary glands:
   a) are present only in females
   b) depend on estrogen for growth and development
   c) are considered to be primary sex organs
   d) All of the above

3. The ovaries are:
   a) the site of egg production
   b) attached to the fallopian tubes
   c) located adjacent to the kidneys
   d) All of the above

4. Which of the following is *not* true concerning egg production?
   a) Ova are present in a female fetus at birth.
   b) Ova are produced through meiosis of oocytes.
   c) Oocytes are contained within ovarian follicles.
   d) Ovulation is the release of an ovum from a graafian follicle.

5. Which of the following is true of the corpus luteum?
   a) It is active in the ovarian follicular stage.
   b) It is formed prior to ovulation.
   c) It produces progesterone.
   d) All of the above

6. The fallopian tubes:
   a) are the site of fertilization
   b) are held in place by the broad ligament
   c) function for peristalsis by contraction of its smooth muscle layer
   d) All of the above

7. Which of the following is true about the anatomy of the uterus?
   a) It contains the myometrium, an outer muscular layer.
   b) It contains the endometrium, an inner mucosal layer.
   c) It is connected to the vagina at the cervix.
   d) All of the above

8. Which of the following is *not* a component of the external female genitalia?
   a) labia minora
   b) mons
   c) vagina
   d) clitoris

9. The testes contain the:
   a) seminal vesicles
   b) epididymis
   c) seminiferous tubules
   d) All of the above

10. The seminal vessels include the:
    a) vas deferens
    b) seminal vesicles
    c) prostate gland
    d) All of the above

11. Which of the following is *not* a component of the male external genitalia?
    a) Cowper's glands
    b) scrotum
    c) penis
    d) phallus

12. The most internal component of the penis is the:
    a) glans
    b) urethra
    c) foreskin
    d) corpus cavernosum

13. The ovarian cycle:
    a) leads to ovulation
    b) is divided into follicular and luteal stages
    c) includes development of the corpus luteum
    d) All of the above

14. The proliferative stage of the menstrual cycle:
    a) occurs only following pregnancy
    b) precedes the ovarian cycle
    c) produces a thickened endometrium
    d) All of the above

15. Erection of the penis results from:
    a) sympathetic innervation
    b) constriction of arteries and dilation of veins
    c) constriction of veins and dilation of arteries
    d) decreased parasympathetic innervation

16. Which of the following is *not* true regarding the components of semen?
    a) Semen contains sperm produced in the testes.
    b) Semen contains nutrients, hormones, and enzymes produced by the seminal vesicles.
    c) Semen contains an alkaline substance produced by the prostate gland.
    d) All of the above are true.

17. Which of the following is the normal functioning sequence of events for males during copulation?
    a) sexual arousal, erection, ejaculation, detumescence
    b) detumescence, erection, sexual arousal, ejaculation
    c) sexual arousal, detumescence, erection, ejaculation
    d) sexual arousal, detumescence, erection, ejaculation

18. Which of the following is a normal female sexual response?
    a) erectile tissue response of the clitoris and nipples
    b) mucous production by Skene's glands
    c) muscle contractions of the vaginal tract and cervix
    d) All of the above

19. Penetration of the egg by sperm is made possible by:
    a) the acidic pH of the vagina
    b) the sperm flagella
    c) enzymes contained in a sperm structure called the acrosome
    d) the corpus luteum

20. At the point of implantation, the developing fertilized egg is called a:
    a) zygote
    b) gastrula
    c) blastula
    d) fetus

21. Formation of the placenta:
    a) is initiated by implantation
    b) marks the beginning of pregnancy
    c) allows for nourishment of the developing embryo
    d) All of the above

22. What hormone has a similar structure to pollutants thought to have a detrimental effect on normal male embryological development?
    a) androgen
    b) estrogen
    c) progesterone
    d) testosterone

23. Sexually transmitted diseases can be spread through:
    a) copulation
    b) infectious viruses, bacteria, or protistans
    c) oral and anal sex
    d) All of the above

24. Which of the following is not a disorder associated with pregnancy?
    a) fibroids
    b) placenta previa
    c) ectopic implantation
    d) All of the above are disorders associated with pregnancy.

25. Age-related changes in the reproductive system:
    a) usually have no effect on sexual function
    b) always decrease the sex drive
    c) are most commonly associated with changes in the endocrine and urinary systems
    d) All of the above